# A CITY RECOVERS

**THE PRESS**

CHRISTCHURCH TWO YEARS AFTER THE QUAKES

Text by **Paul Gorman** and *Press* journalists
Images by *Press* and **Fairfax** photographers
Picture research by **Jude Tewnion**

RANDOM HOUSE
NEW ZEALAND

# FOREWORD

It gives me great pleasure to provide the foreword to *A City Recovers*. This is *The Press*' third book on the Canterbury earthquakes — a fact that serves to illustrate the enormity of the events we've experienced over the past two and a half years.

While the first title, *The Big Quake*, was naturally a snapshot in time of the damage caused by the September 4 event, and the civil defence and community efforts in the initial response, and the second, *Earthquake! Christchurch 22 February 2011*, documented the heartbreak and devastation of the second major quake, this book captures the way our community has pulled together as the exciting process of recovery has gained momentum.

I have a vivid memory of touring the CBD red zone, and Sydenham, with then Defence Minister Dr Wayne Mapp on Saturday, four days after February 22. As we stood amid the rubble on Colombo Street in Sydenham, looking back toward the city centre, the sheer scale of the building damage really hit home.

The security alarm in the badly damaged Work and Income building at 387 Colombo Street was ringing into its fifth day, and its batteries were fading into a mournful, half-hearted drone. The Ascot TV building across the road at 400 Colombo Street, which had been cordoned off for safety reasons following the September 4 event, had been left in no doubt this time as to whether repair was a viable option — it was practically destroyed.

Today the site at 400 Colombo Street is one of the colourful temporary community gardens developed by the wonderful volunteers of the Greening the Rubble Trust. Ornately planted, with comfortable seating, it is a bright and popular gathering point for coffee and a chat — and even has a boules (petanque) court.

The trust's work of creating temporary public parks and gardens on the sites of demolished buildings, through licence agreements with site owners, and sponsorship of construction materials and design, is a great example of the way a group of community-minded Cantabrians have seen the difficult events we've been through as an opportunity for making their neighbours' lives better.

Whether 400 Colombo Street is built on soon or at a later date, the tremendous loss of so many older buildings has left us in no doubt about the requirements of future buildings in Christchurch. And those older buildings

Artworks and graffiti sprang up on empty walls at vacant sites across the city after the earthquakes, like this piece along Colombo St in Sydenham.

**KIRK HARGREAVES**

that remain must be strengthened and able to cope with future events. We must build high-quality buildings on strong foundations. The buildings constructed in the aftermath of this quake have been built to a building code that the engineers and scientists have designed to better cope with severe earthquakes.

An important lesson from the earthquakes is that the building structure is only as good as the platform on which it is built. The land and foundations are key factors in determining the survival of that structure.

The insurance of land in New Zealand is something that is not available in other parts of the world. The Earthquake Commission (EQC) is a unique institution that has positioned New Zealand well to recover from a disaster of this magnitude. One key aspect has been its investment in the science and its focus on land as a platform for building. EQC has coordinated a major geotechnical investigation of the land under the Canterbury region. This systematic and scientific approach has given us perhaps the most sophisticated knowledge of the subsurface of any urban region in the world. This will benefit Canterbury for decades to come.

In June 2011, the Government assessed the information about the impact of the earthquakes on the land in Canterbury. We decided that, in the long term, rebuilding on poor-quality land would mean that we would be doomed to repeat the mistakes of the past.

The designation of residential red zones was based on the information collated through the EQC investigation. The Crown made a voluntary offer to purchase properties in the most severely damaged suburbs at the pre-quake Rating Valuation. The net cost to the taxpayers of that endeavour will exceed $1 billion.

Homeowners in the red zone have seen and embraced the chance to move on and rebuild with confidence on safe land. Zoning the land was a project that will give long-term confidence in the greater Christchurch building stock.

The Government worked through the challenges that confronted us in a systematic manner. I was often asked to hurry decisions. What is clear in retrospect is that good decisions that took a few weeks longer for investigating all options and their long-term viability are better placed to last the test of time.

As further assessment of residential red zones has been done, engineers see a clear difference between that land and that designated green and appropriate for habitation. This means we can rebuild with confidence in the condition of all land not zoned red. This includes the 14 per cent of residential land in Christchurch classified as Technical Category 3 (TC3).

TC3 is a performance standard which will ensure that in the event of a major quake the house will perform as well as a house on land less susceptible to seismic damage. This requires stronger foundations.

Engineers have studied what would happen if a September 2010-level quake were to hit the city again. The elimination of the residential red zones, the loss of building stock below building code performance standards, and the adherence to high standards means that such a quake would not have anywhere near the level of damage to property and financial loss. Neither would it be as likely to endanger life.

New Zealanders' extremely high levels of insurance have provided the vital capital to rebuild. We can now demonstrate that our rebuild will significantly de-risk the greater Christchurch area for future insurance contracts. That will ultimately help to keep insurance affordable and ensure sufficient cover is available to progress the recovery.

The CBD blueprint was unveiled on July 30, 2012, and has given direction to construction of the new central city. Certainty about the future shape and geography of the city makes it easier for investors to use their capital to build on a particular site.

The Christchurch Central Development Unit, or CCDU, was formed to create a consistent and coherent plan to redevelop the central city. It was also charged with leading the core government-sector developments and attracting the private-sector investment alongside it.

The first task was the delivery of the blueprint within 100 days. The decision to design a comprehensive blueprint was based on a number of factors. There was recognition that a city with more than 70 per cent of buildings demolished should be rebuilt as a city of the 21st century — not a replica of the past. It has to be a liveable, walkable city that will be attractive to live, work and play in. Many have remarked that before the earthquakes the city was struggling to attract people, and that was reflected in a decline of retail and hospitality in its centre.

We knew both local and central government would need new buildings. We knew that where those buildings went would impact on the decisions of investors. For example, hoteliers were anxious to know where a convention centre would be placed. The location of the courts and police station would impact on the legal fraternity. These core civic assets are the anchors around which a city develops.

The plan we revealed gives shape to the city based on international best practice urban design. It also reflects the more than 100,000 submissions received in the 'Share an Idea' consultation with Cantabrians. Their vision of a greener city will be reflected in the urban frame, which will create a corridor for pedestrians and cyclists to access the city. To give effect to the plan, we have an extensive purchasing plan in progress to accumulate the necessary land holdings. This plan has restored the supply and demand balance in the commercial property market.

While the price of land has fallen dramatically following the earthquakes, it has not collapsed, as could be expected in a post-disaster scenario. This is a reflection of the feeling of confidence that the city can be successfully rebuilt and realistic returns generated.

There will always be arguments about the market price of land, but it's worth noting that the Crown's approach to Christchurch is more generous than the approach taken following the Napier earthquake. The date set for assessing compensation for Napier landowners was February 4, 1931 — the day *after* the earthquake.

We have underpinned the market value of land and are taking out the excess supply. This allows development to be concentrated, creating a tight core to build out from rather than encouraging an inconsistent patchwork of development. This is one of the reasons the CBD plan has generated considerable confidence in the future of Christchurch.

Large numbers of expressions of interest have been received for the convention-centre precinct and other anchor projects in the CBD, with a mixture of domestic and international participants competing to be at the centre of a revived tourism industry in Canterbury. We know from market interest that high-quality new hotels will greatly enhance our capacity for tourism and business travel.

Visitors to Christchurch will be attracted by new cultural and entertainment facilities. The CCDU plan envisages a high-quality performing arts and entertainment complex across Victoria Square from the convention centre. New sporting facilities will make Christchurch a destination for large sporting events. Those anchor projects are vital for making Canterbury a great place to live.

This is also why the Avon River precinct is a key anchor project. By creating a corridor of green space for people in the urban environment, the river will be similar to the waterfront in Auckland or Wellington.

Outside the anchor projects, private-sector investment is thriving. Prior to the earthquakes, Cashel Street Mall had replaced most of its high-end fashion stores with discount goods outlets and small retailers. Today we have major investors competing to build their visions in that space.

Christchurch's reconstruction will be led by investors making decisions based on a confident future, consistent with the vision of being a vibrant and positive centre of the South Island.

The earthquakes smashed apart the core infrastructure around roads, wastewater, stormwater and drinking water. Typically, that infrastructure takes decades to develop as a city grows and expands. We have the challenge of building up that infrastructure while maintaining service to 180,000 households.

That work will continue for five years and will leave a legacy of the best designed and mapped infrastructure in the country. Pipes and sewers are being laid with modern technology. Work that had been completed between the September 2010 and February 2011 earthquakes was largely undamaged by the major shake. Modern materials will leave Christchurch with a more resilient system.

Above those pipes that are under repair lie the roads that carry people about their daily business. Anyone driving around Christchurch can tell you that. Wearing my other hard hat as Transport Minister, I can point to the recently completed stage one of the Christchurch Southern Motorway. People regularly report to me that journeys that once took 40 minutes now take just 15.

Freight is flowing more freely into the Port of Lyttelton, and while the port has suffered major damage, and repair work will take some time, Lyttelton itself will benefit from a major reclamation built from the rubble taken from the CBD. That presents the ultimate opportunity to move the port out of the inner basin and in the longer term develop the town's waterfront into a recreation and tourism hub for the city.

The scale of development in the Canterbury region is unprecedented. We have a very bright future ahead of us. As the global economy recovers we will be well positioned for high productivity and export-driven economic growth.

The most important part of that future will be the people who live here. As I've said at numerous public gatherings over the past two and a half years, the strongest legacy for me in how Christchurch has responded to the quakes is the way all people, from every walk of life, are now going about their daily lives slightly differently, just happy to be here, and working at improving our city.

People go to work via different routes, to jobs in different places, very often doing business differently to the way they were before September 2010 and February 2011. And for the most part, despite numerous personal challenges, Christchurch's residents have embraced and even relished the challenge. They've done Canterbury proud.

**The Hon. Gerry Brownlee**
*Minister for Canterbury Earthquake Recovery*

The quakes were never going to stop the simple pleasures, like just kicking a ball about. This Nike temporary football pitch was set up on the corner of Colombo and Hereford streets in November 2012.

**RICHARD COSGROVE**

# CONTENTS

The lost city: A pre-quake view of a corner of Cathedral Square, including the former Post Office Building and the Royal Exchange Building or Regent Theatre.
**STACY SQUIRES**

# INTRODUCTION
## THE NEW NORMAL

*Ric Stevens*

It took generations of pioneers, builders, entrepreneurs and city politicians 160 years to build the Christchurch that we knew on the morning of February 22, 2011. At lunchtime that day, it took 20 seconds of seismic activity to destroy it. In less than half a minute, about 1300 commercial buildings and 10,000 homes were wrecked immediately or damaged beyond repair. Tragically, 185 people died or were mortally wounded. The lives of half a million Cantabrians were changed forever by the magnitude 6.3 earthquake that struck at 12.51pm that day.

**THIS BOOK IS** not so much about the earthquake, though, as about what happened next. The February 2011 earthquake was not a single event. It was part of a seismic sequence that started in the early hours of September 4, 2010, when a magnitude 7.1 quake tore across the countryside around Greendale, west of the city, causing widespread damage. The aftershocks of these two major upheavals continued for two years and numbered more than 10,000. Possibly they are not over yet. In those days, weeks, months, and years, half a million Cantabrians learned to adjust to what they called a 'new normal'.

No one who lived in the greater Christchurch area through this time had to ask what the phrase 'new normal' meant. It meant readjusting one's hopes and aspirations, picking up the pieces, questioning life's directions and getting on with whatever needed to be done, even as the ground continued to shake. Life would never be the same as before the February quake; it would be a series of compromises and reassessments. Perhaps in time the Canterbury earthquakes will be revealed as not just a geological happening, but as a complex and interlocked series of physical, social and even psychological events, affecting people in different ways but with common underlying themes.

The earthquake seemed to strike at the very heart of Christchurch's identity, particularly as it laid waste to the city's built heritage, much of

Architectural gems: Pre-quake views of the rooftops of, above, the Arts Centre (formerly the University of Canterbury) and, opposite, part of the Provincial Council Buildings complex, both damaged.
**ABOVE: DAVID ALEXANDER**
**OPPOSITE: DAVID HALLETT**

which — some argue — was then cleared away by the ubiquitous diggers with undue haste. The earthquakes showed no respect for heritage values and resulted in what the Historic Places Trust called an 'unprecedented' loss of historic buildings. Whole precincts and streetscapes would not survive. More than a hundred properties on Colombo St alone, for example, were destined to be completely or partially demolished.

In the book *Southern Capital, Christchurch: Towards a City Biography*, edited by Professor John Cookson and Graeme Dunstall (Canterbury University Press, 2000), Cookson writes about Christchurch's sense of identity and its imagined genesis as a settlement of British pilgrims inspired by the ideals of the Church of England. Particularly between 1880 and 1914, he notes, the cityscape — buildings, trees and gardens — matured into English Christchurch, or the Garden City, with the Anglican cathedral at its heart. 'English Christchurch,' Cookson writes, 'has become a look rather than a tradition, distinctiveness conferred by beauties that, mainly because of the topography and architectural legacy, it is not in the power of other cities to emulate.'

As Cookson also points out, the notion of Christchurch Englishness was partly a myth or a figment of imagination. Actually, Christchurch bore little resemblance to real English cities and was always easily identifiable as a colonial town. But, to people who lived in Christchurch and valued their

**LEFT** The Arts Centre is reflected in a window of the Canterbury Museum.
**DAN TOBIN**

**TOP RIGHT** Cranmer Courts, now demolished.
**STACY SQUIRES**

**MIDDLE RIGHT** The Arts Centre's North Quad.
**CARYS MONTEATH**

**BOTTOM RIGHT** Punting on the Avon.
**JOHN KIRK-ANDERSON**

connections with the Anglican settlers, it was English enough. This imagined sense of identity was enhanced and given more substance by the presence of the Gothic revival heritage buildings seen within almost every central city streetscape.

When people talked of Christchurch's 'history', they were sometimes really referring to the heritage of those old English-style structures such as ChristChurch Cathedral, the Arts Centre, the Canterbury Museum and Cranmer Courts. Often, that heritage was linked to their own personal genealogies, family stories and rites of passage. When those buildings were perceived to be threatened, as was the case of the cathedral when the visitors' centre was proposed in 1992, the town erupted in controversy, because something very personal about how Christchurch people saw themselves was seen to be under threat. When some of those buildings were fatally damaged by the February 2011 earthquake, Christchurch's sense of place could only give way to a sense of loss.

And if Cookson was right that the architectural legacy is not within the power of other cities to emulate, equally we might have to accept that much of it is no longer within Christchurch's power to save or replicate. The photograph on the cover of *Southern Capital, Christchurch*, for instance, conveys a scene that will never be seen again. It was obviously chosen to show the contrasts in the Christchurch cityscape of the year 2000: the Gothic architecture of the Provincial Council Buildings (badly damaged by the earthquakes) against the modern PWC building (now demolished), the Forsyth Barr building (future uncertain) and the Farmers carpark (demolished). It was shot from the Amuri Courts parking building on Durham St (demolished).

Not too far away from the site shown in the photograph, on Montreal St, stood Cranmer Courts, a feature on one corner of Cranmer

Square. This complex of buildings, which once housed Christchurch Normal School, was built between 1873 and 1876 in the style that could be broadly covered by the description Christchurch Gothic. Designed by Christchurch architect Samuel C Farr, the buildings were used for teaching and teacher training for nearly a century. They stood empty for a decade before being bought by a developer in 1981 and converted into 22 apartments, which were privately occupied at the time Cranmer Courts was badly damaged by the September 2010 quake and rendered unsafe for occupation.

Residents were divided on whether the complex could be saved, even after each put in more than $30,000 to shore it up. In the words of body-corporate member Rod McKay: 'We've put in almost $1 million to maintain a brick wall for backgrounds for tourists' photos.' Most residents seemed to feel that saving the complex was just 'not viable'. Various attempts to raise funds to save it fell through and, despite vocal opposition from the heritage lobby, the complex was destroyed in late 2012.

Other buildings lost throughout the city included the former Christchurch Girls' High School at 40 Armagh St, the former Canterbury Public Library buildings on Cambridge Tce, the Theosophical Society Building at 267 Cambridge Tce, St Paul's-Trinity-Pacific Presbyterian Church at the corner of Cashel and Madras streets, the Cathedral Grammar School main block at 2 Chester St West, the former Colombo St Wesleyan Church and nearby former Sydenham Post Office, the Durham St Methodist Church, the Canterbury Times and Star building on Gloucester St, St Elmo Courts at 47 Hereford St, the T&G building at 190–192 Hereford St, Perry's Occidental Hotel at 208 Hereford St, St John the Baptist Church at 234 Hereford St, the triangular ANZ Bank building at 188 High St, the Repertory Theatre at 146 Kilmore St, Manchester Courts at 158–160 Manchester St, the MED building at 218 Manchester St, the Oxford Tce Baptist Church, the Carlton Hotel on the corner of Bealey Ave and Papanui Rd, and the old part of St George's Hospital.

In addition to ChristChurch Cathedral, intended for partial demolition, buildings that were lost in Cathedral Square included The Press building, the Lyttelton Times building, Warner's Hotel and the old Regent Theatre. Many significant buildings in Lyttelton were lost, including the internationally significant Timeball Station.

Precious little, it sometimes seemed, could be saved, but in fact Christchurch will always be recognisably the city it once was. Hagley Park and the Christchurch Botanic Gardens will always be the jewels in its crown, and a 2012 debate about whether the Hagley Oval might be developed into a test-cricket venue recalled many a pre-quake debate on the city's traditional view of itself. The former university complex making up the Arts Centre and significant parts of the Canterbury Provincial Council Buildings

Now gone: These three historic buildings, from top, the ANZ Chambers on Lichfield and High streets, the Orion Building on Manchester St and St Paul's Trinity Pacific Church on Cashel St have all been lost.

**TOP: DAVID ALEXANDER**

**MIDDLE AND BOTTOM: STACY SQUIRES**

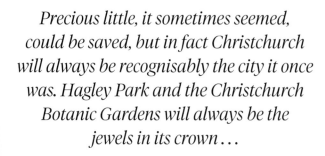

*Precious little, it sometimes seemed, could be saved, but in fact Christchurch will always be recognisably the city it once was. Hagley Park and the Christchurch Botanic Gardens will always be the jewels in its crown…*

are being rebuilt. Unlike Cranmer Courts, its near neighbour the Peterborough Building, a later complex also converted into apartments, was saved by an international consortium that decided to repair the structure even if it meant losing money. In October 2012, the Christchurch City Council voted to save the 40-year-old Town Hall complex and its outstanding concert chamber, although whether it could be salvaged remained to be seen.

**IF CHRISTCHURCH'S SENSE** of place or identity had been challenged or lost with the destruction of so much of the city centre, the people's vision of what should replace it was made known during the 2011 'Share an Idea' consultation exercise conducted by the Christchurch City Council. This was consolidated into a city council plan that imagined a 'city in a garden'. After the government-appointed Canterbury Earthquake Recovery Authority (CERA) took over responsibility for the city rebuild, its Christchurch Central Development Unit (CCDU) produced a blueprint, in late 2012, that in part delivered on that vision, providing for a smaller central business district, 'framed' on all sides by the Avon River and wide corridors of green space. Whole city blocks, many of them already wastelands cleared of rubble, were set aside to become

# The Avon river and a new green 'frame' define Christchurch's new compact city centre.

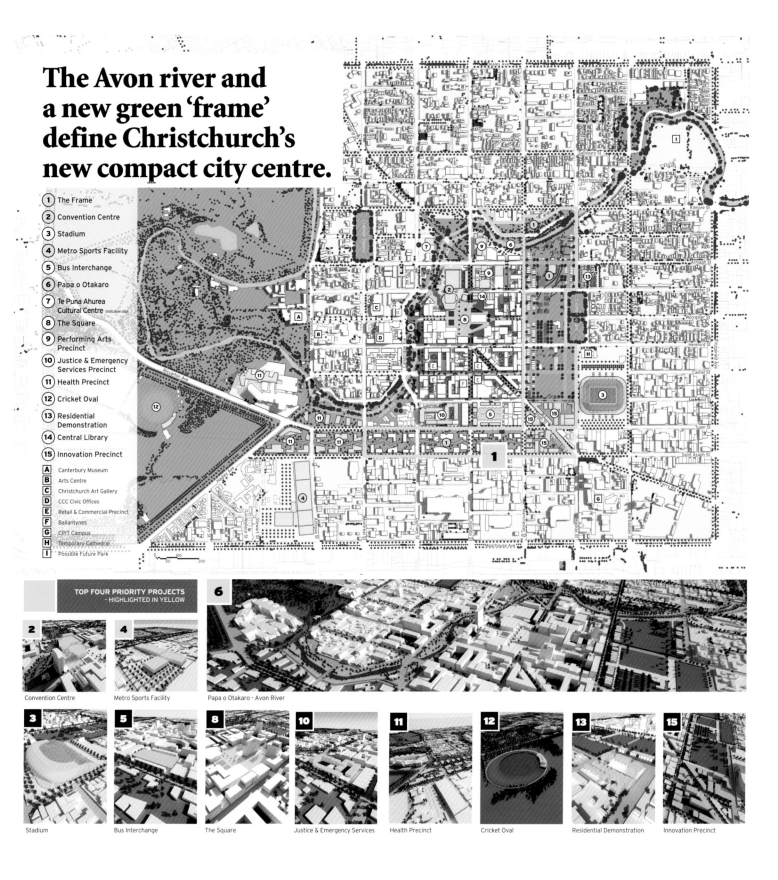

1. The Frame
2. Convention Centre
3. Stadium
4. Metro Sports Facility
5. Bus Interchange
6. Papa o Otakaro
7. Te Puna Ahurea Cultural Centre (indicative site)
8. The Square
9. Performing Arts Precinct
10. Justice & Emergency Services Precinct
11. Health Precinct
12. Cricket Oval
13. Residential Demonstration
14. Central Library
15. Innovation Precinct

A. Canterbury Museum
B. Arts Centre
C. Christchurch Art Gallery
D. CCC Civic Offices
E. Retail & Commercial Precinct
F. Ballantynes
G. CPIT Campus
H. Temporary Cathedral
I. Possible Future Park

**TOP FOUR PRIORITY PROJECTS**
- HIGHLIGHTED IN YELLOW

2 Convention Centre

4 Metro Sports Facility

6 Papa o Otakaro - Avon River

3 Stadium

5 Bus Interchange

8 The Square

10 Justice & Emergency Services

11 Health Precinct

12 Cricket Oval

13 Residential Demonstration

15 Innovation Precinct

# A smaller central business district "framed" by green space, summarises the plan

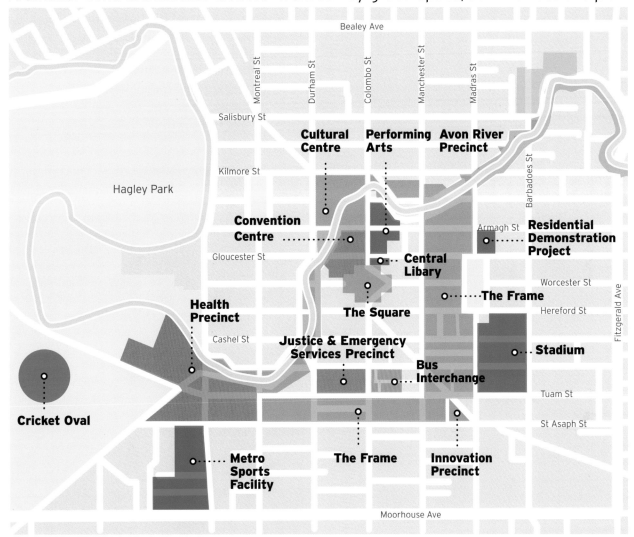

The CERA blueprint, released in late 2012, proposed a green 'frame' for the city centre but left the details of the anchor projects such as the stadium and the Convention Centre deliberately vague. What they will look like, and who will pay for them, is not yet known.

**CERA**

attractive parklands. Around the centre, new 'precincts' and projects would appear: cultural, arts and metro sports centres; facilities for health services and courts; an 'innovation precinct'; a residential area, and a new, covered multi-purpose stadium.

The aim of the plan is to draw more activities into the centre. The core CBD will be only about a dozen city blocks: virtually all of the projects envisaged — including the stadium — lie within the Four Avenues. Cathedral Square will be utterly transformed, and may well be considered the centrepiece of this blueprint, literally and figuratively. The new convention-centre complex, with shops, hotels and plaza, will front onto the Square and extend back over Gloucester St and the next block all the way to Victoria Square. A new central library will be built on the site of the Camelot Hotel, and the Square itself will be made 'greener' and closed to through-traffic.

The plan does not deal with the future of the badly damaged cathedral, which is still a matter for the Anglican Church. The rebuilt Square is likely to be dominated by the sheer mass of the convention-centre complex, which will have two hotels, the capacity to host 2000 people, and the potential for three conferences to be run at once.

The CCDU plan ignores the desire articulated by Christchurch mayor Bob Parker for a light rail system to run initially between the university and the central city. Buses are the preferred future of public transport in the city, along with ample provision for walking and cycling. The planners deliberately avoided suggesting a site and form for an earthquake memorial, feeling that this would take time and more reflection.

It will take years for the future shape of Christchurch to be determined, but it became clearer during 2012 that a very different city will emerge from the upheaval. Whole streets and even suburbs in the eastern part of the city began to disappear, along with the human stories and memories that had been associated with them. About 10,000 homes — mainly in the east but also on the Port Hills and in pockets of other areas — were red-zoned, bought by the government, and the occupants prepared to move out.

Some took the opportunity to leave town altogether, but it soon became apparent where most people were going. Towns and settlements that had already been growing outside the city boundaries, mainly in the Selwyn and Waimakariri districts, began to expand even more rapidly. It looked like people were seeking solid ground. The already growing town of Rolleston, for example, had been badly shaken up by the September 2010 quake, but had suffered comparatively little structural damage. It began to boom.

Within Christchurch itself, the western suburbs survived with less damage and these

*It will take years for the future shape of Christchurch to be determined, but it became clearer during 2012 that a very different city will emerge from the upheaval.*

*The Press* was one of the first businesses back into the former central city red zone, when it occupied the new Press House on Gloucester St in 2012.

**CARYS MONTEATH**

areas also benefited from the relocation of many businesses from the city centre. Addington and Riccarton, for example, became home to many of the white-collar workers who had previously trooped each day into the old CBD. The city's distress, however, also affected the property market. With lower supply and higher but patchy demand, it was obvious that both rents and property prices would begin to rise, and they did, although the government sought to downplay complaints of a housing crisis.

The year 2012 included what could accurately be described as a winter of discontent, prompting Canterbury Earthquake Recovery Minister Gerry Brownlee to complain about the 'carping and moaning' of people with a certain type of land category — he later apologised for the comment. But after two years of living with uncertainty, and with little opportunity to move on with their lives, many people were finding life difficult.

Undoubtedly, insurance was one of the most difficult and personally affecting issues that Cantabrians had to deal with. The Earthquake Commission (EQC) received more than 459,000 claims related to the Canterbury earthquakes. By the end of 2012 it had settled fewer than a quarter of them. It referred to its liabilities for the land, building and contents components of each property as 'exposures' (more than one of which could be included in a single claim). It had settled 81 per cent of content exposures, but only 31 per cent of building exposures and 26 per cent of land exposures. Some claimants also had to deal with their private insurance companies in addition to the government insurer.

*The Press* conducted a survey coinciding with the second anniversary of the September 2010 earthquake. The survey by Opinions Market Research of 400 adults found that 50 per cent were very, or extremely, dissatisfied with EQC's performance, while more than one-third of those who had filed a claim were unhappy with their private insurers. The gloom was more pronounced in the badly hit east of Christchurch. EQC's general manager of customer service, Bruce Emson, pointed out that the number of claims and exposures was matched historically only by Hurricane Katrina in the US. To put EQC's job into context, the number of claims was more than double the total number of claims faced by the Commission for every event in its entire history prior to September 4, 2010.

The same survey indicated a generation gap in the way people were affected by the earthquakes. It found that 90 per cent of people under 30, lacking significant property, had not even put in an insurance claim, while their elders were still struggling against the bureacracy of insurance companies and EQC. It was therefore easier for young people to move on and many did (although many more stayed), but the concern about what Christchurch still had to offer the young was troubling even Mayor Parker.

In November 2012 he urged the government to rethink its blueprint for the rebuilt city, lest it become little more than a 'glossy rest home'. Parker said the plans were not bold enough, and the community's vision expressed through 'Share an Idea' had been 'compromised away' by the CCDU blueprint.

The combination of the ageing population and the unprecedented number of young people leaving Christchurch, Parker said, meant that in about 20 years more than half the population of the city would be over the age of 65. He had noticed many of his friends' children were also relocating to Wellington, Auckland and Sydney because Christchurch no longer catered for their needs. Among his suggested solutions was moving the university back into the central city — something the university has consistently ruled out.

By the beginning of 2013 some commercial buildings had been reopened in the city centre, but they were precious few in number — Ballantynes, the new Press House, the Ibis Hotel, Calendar Girls, Les Mills, Alice in Videoland. The city rebuild was taking longer than expected.

It was not all doom and gloom, however. As the second anniversary of the February 2011 earthquake approached, the mood of the city was that things were about to change; that the long-promised rebuilding was indeed on the way. This impression was supported by successive survey indicators that suggested increased activity in everything from retail spending to hiring intentions to building consents. An employment drive in the UK and Ireland had reportedly hooked as many as 600 tradespeople to work on the rebuild. People in Christchurch looked forward to an influx of new arrivals to give the city a more cosmopolitan edge.

In October 2012, Christchurch hosted a festival of transitional architecture in which a Luxcity event illuminated the broken city centre with sculptures of light. The pop-up mall of shipping containers converted into temporary shops in Cashel Mall, the Gap Filler initiative and attempts to 'Green the Rubble' also showed that the impetus for regeneration and renewal was beginning at grass roots, rather than simply being imposed from above. The people of Christchurch were beginning to look to the future. ∎

# THE HUMAN TOLL

## A TOLL THAT CANNOT BE MEASURED

*Olivia Carville*

How does one measure the human toll of a natural disaster? Can suffering or heartache be quantified? Tallying up the crude number of fatalities is straightforward — weighing the grief of those left behind, or those scarred for life, is much less simple.

**GRIEF ISN'T SOMETHING** that can be tamed or disciplined. It has a maddening, merciless will of its own. Over the years it may abate, but at any moment it can stir. Those shouldering grief know that in an instant it can strike. It tarnishes birthdays, sucks the magic out of Christmas, and threatens to darken the most significant moments of a life. With a flick of its tail, grief can bring you to your knees. It is an incalculable beast that has nested in Christchurch and will continue to morph and stretch as it chooses.

The 2011 earthquake stole much from many. Uninvited, it snaked its way through the city and snatched its heart in seconds. Grown men cried. Grisly cracks tore through family homes. Entire suburbs were lost.

The official death toll rests at 185. But the statistics do little justice to the extent of the grief and do not even begin to measure the human impact. One mother held her dead eight-month-old son in her arms for seven hours; another sat at the end of her driveway all night waiting for her 14-year-old to come home from school. Parents of international students flew across the world to hold a vigil at the smouldering CTV site, praying for a miracle.

Two years on, our grief is still red-faced and raw. It can be seen in the weathered eyes of a young widow and in the face of a paraplegic looking down at her lifeless body. It is represented in the elderly man's caravan parked outside his crooked home and in the irate protester demanding his voice be heard. The human toll encompasses the seriously injured, the bereaved and the ordinary Cantabrians who lost their way of life, if not their actual lives.

# THE SURVIVORS

**CHEATING DEATH COMES** with its sacrifices — and for some the price was very high. There is a group of people whose lives changed irrevocably on February 22, 2011.

Those worst injured in the Christchurch earthquake all share stories of horror that end as miraculous tales of survival. Some spent hours trapped in the rubble, banging and yelling to be heard. One mother was wrongly pronounced dead at the scene, a father had his legs amputated with a hacksaw in the ruins of a building. Some were brought back to life on the medical table and some spent weeks in an induced coma with anxious family members pacing at their bedside. Most of these survivors' bones were crushed beyond repair; they were bleeding internally and barely breathing when they reached medical centres.

Of the thousands hurt in the quake, 23 people suffered critical, life-

changing injuries. Three lost both their legs. Three were paralysed. Many were severely crushed or were inflicted with serious brain and nerve damage. These are the people who threatened to drive the death toll over 200.

The 23 share experiences that few in the world can relate to and they have been united by their survival. Every month, the wounded fellowship meet in a cafe in Christchurch to share their progress and vent their frustrations and uncertainty about the future. Three members of the group spoke openly of their life two years on. These are their stories.

Helen Grice was struck down by her chimney in the quake. Her 15-year-old son found her beneath the rubble in the lounge, and builders from an adjacent site helped haul her out. She spent hours lying against her ironing board with her bloodied and bruised body covered in frozen peas and meat as she waited for an ambulance. The 51-year-old mother of four was paralysed from the bra-line down.

Helen feels like an outsider in her family and a burden to her husband.

There have been days when she wished she hadn't survived the earthquake at all. Her once exuberant personality has cowered with the loss of her legs. Her laughter is no longer as loud.

The quake delivered Helen a life sentence in a wheelchair and tore her family apart. Her lifeless feet no longer fill the shoes of the mother she once was, and an unwelcome dynamic has settled on her household.

'There are two families now. There is my husband and me, and then there's him and the kids. I don't fit in with the kids any more.'

Helen has lost her role as the 'go to' parent. Her teenage children no longer ask her for money or permission to go out, she can't just jump in the car and pick them up from the mall or drop them off at their friends' houses, and they have faced their own grief and anxieties that she has not been able to share.

She was aware she wouldn't be able to just wheel herself back into her old life, but said she never knew 'it was going to be this hard'.

'I don't think my kids really understand what sort of a battle it is every day. I love them for being teenagers, but at times they can really hurt me.' She hopes that with time the fractured relationships will heal.

'I hope they had enough grounding and sense of family before the quake that they will come back to me again.'

Helen was disappointed there was so little support for families struggling to cope with life-changing injuries and said she pleaded for a family group-counselling session, but was denied assistance by ACC. It was not the only time she felt ACC had let her family down. When she first returned home, they delivered a single-paraplegic bed and refused to replace it with a double, despite the fact that Helen had slept next to her husband during 28 years of marriage. It cost Ben Grice $4000 to buy his own single-paraplegic bed to push up against his wife's and allow the couple to sleep together again.

He has been her rock and guiding light through the past two years. Up until the accident, their relationship had the hallmarks of a fairy-tale romance. He was her first-ever boyfriend, who later became her husband and then the father of her children. Now, in a cruel twist of fate, he has stepped into the role of her carer. Just as the glimmer of a life without dependent children was beginning to take shape on the horizon, the Grices' future was pulled from under them. But the accident has not fully dampened the romance.

'He still believes my views are important and he does things to make me feel like I'm still lovely,' Helen said as she fluffed her hair. 'He makes me feel like I'm desirable, and I think he's pretty hot too.'

The pair have fought to maintain their sex life through the tragedy, although she said it had transformed from spontaneous desire to a 'planned rendezvous'. Even with an unfaltering love, the past two years have not been rosy for the couple and Helen admits there have been dark days.

Just after the quake, she recalls telling her husband she would understand if he wanted a divorce. He reminded her of their wedding vows and told her she was being an idiot. During her recovery she told him it would have been easier to 'have just died'. He reminded her that she was his best friend and that he couldn't afford to lose a best friend. And when she had a bowel 'mistake' at home late one night, he had to step in.

'I was blubbering and sobbing as he was cleaning me and he stopped and

TOP February earthquake survivor Ken Hird woke up in hospital paralysed after a horror bike accident during an aftershock. He has slowly learned how to move again.
PHOTO SUPPLIED

BOTTOM Ken Hird, with his dog Molly, is back on his bike, though he says his sense of feeling has completely changed following the accident.
IAIN MCGREGOR

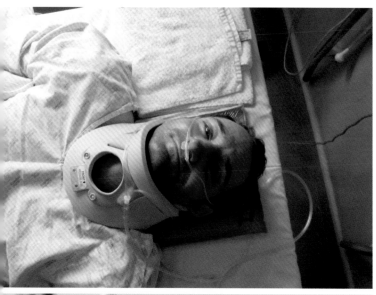

said, "Look at me. You know I love you," and he just kept cleaning,' she said through tears.

There have also been days when Helen has thought: 'This is too dark. This is too deep and there is no way of climbing out of this.' And at times she has looked at her husband and felt a stab of guilt. 'I see him so tired, just holding it together, and I feel like such a burden. Sometimes I look at him and it just breaks my heart.'

Helen has sadness for what she has lost, but there is no anger in her tone. Looking down at her inert, broken body, she says: 'You poor thing. You're just so battered and no matter what we do, you're not going to move. It's all over for you.'

Life will carry on for Helen, and she has no doubt there will be many happy moments. But for now she is concentrating on piecing together what was unfairly broken.

Ken Hird was biking around his neighbourhood after the February quake, checking on the elderly, when an aftershock ripped the ground apart beneath his wheels. He was propelled over the handlebars and his head rammed into the jagged edge of the tar-seal, breaking his neck in three places. The 51-year-old father of four was revived at the scene and woke up the next day completely paralysed. Slowly, over the past two years, he has learned how to move again.

Ken's well-worn and weathered hands have been rendered useless. The normal, middle-aged Kiwi bloke who is now trapped in the body of a crippled old man fears for the future. His injuries may not have stolen his ability to walk, but they have left him a shadow of his former self. The maintenance engineer used to mow the lawns, bike to work, and had DIY in his blood. Now his movements are arduous and restrained. He drags the right-hand side of his body, can no longer button his own shirt, and is reduced to taking a daily afternoon nap.

When Ken's neck snapped, his sensory message systems were wiped and he woke 15 hours after the accident completely paralysed from the neck down. Like a baby, he had to be taught how to control his body and walk again. Ken's damaged thought processes were laid bare as he slowly explains the physical realities of living with trauma.

'My injury is a bit like an iceberg. People see 10 per cent of it but they don't see the other 90 per cent. I feel like I have been catapulted into old age.'

Every step is a challenge and every movement soaks up an immense amount of effort. His weakened muscles and numbed sensory message systems have left mundane daily activities such as mowing lawns, sawing a piece of timber, climbing stairs or going for a run impossible to conquer. And, unmercifully, his memories taunt him by reminding him of a time when he could do it all.

'Old memories tell me I can do it, I think I can do it and remember myself doing it, but my body can no longer keep up,' he says, looking down at his hands as they sit limply in his lap.

His sense of feeling was completely altered by the injury, his hands have lost all their dexterity, and when he touches things they feel different to how they once did. When he tries to pull his cellphone out of his pocket he often finds himself with a fistful of lining. He knows his dog should feel soft and warm, but when he touches her fur it feels rough and coarse. To remind himself of how she truly feels, he lifts her paw and brushes it against his cheek, where the nerve endings are largely unaffected. 'See, that's it,' he smiles.

The Christchurch father has shouldered an onslaught of emotional and physical hurdles since the quake, but is steadfast in his belief that if given the opportunity he would not go back. He feels honoured to have been given a rare insight into the world of stroke victims, the disabled and the elderly, and is sincerely grateful for his 'second chance at life'.

'I understand a wider group of people now and I am privileged to know them and am inspired by them. I wouldn't turn back the clock because of the people I have met along the way.'

Looking forward, Ken is determined to walk away, albeit slowly, from what has been a soul-destroying two-year journey.

He knows his family has paid for his debilitating injuries. His relationship with his wife Susan has aged before its time. The couple grieve

Andrea Robinson (left) and Marnie Holbrook were two of the people who saved Ken Hird on February 22, 2011, after he broke his neck in three places in a cycling accident.
DAVID HALLETT

*'I understand a wider group of people now and I am privileged to know them and am inspired by them. I wouldn't turn back the clock because of the people I have met along the way.'*

for their past romance. They no longer sleep cuddled together because Ken twitches sporadically throughout the night, and he can no longer hold her hand because he has lost control over how hard he squeezes it.

'It's just the touch, putting my hand on his arm and he can't feel it. The little things change the big things,' Susan Hird says.

The chance for Ken to improve or progress physically is nearing an end and he now volunteers to work with those recovering from spinal injuries at Burwood Hospital, where he himself spent months after the quake. Walking from his old hospital room to the gym instils in him the confidence to believe anything is possible. What used to appear as a daunting and unattainable distance is now relatively effortless. He has also, incredibly, managed to conquer his fears, get back on a bike and ride again.

The next stage of his recovery will not be about mourning for the past but 'finding a new way through life'.

Bev Edwards was eating lunch in a cafe in Sydenham when the February 2011 earthquake struck. The roof of the cafe collapsed, killing the elderly woman sitting next to her and leaving Bev pinned in the rubble with a broken back. She is now paralysed from the waist down.

For one-year-old Nicholas, Nanny has always been on wheels. The exuberant toddler clambers over Bev's wheelchair like it is a jungle gym. He shoves her feet off the footrest, plants his cushioned bum down on it and curls his arms around her lifeless legs.

Nicholas has no pity or regret for Nanny. Her wheelchair is all he has ever known and he is quite content with her rolling around the house. But the toddler could not know that Nanny grieves for the moments she has lost with him. She will never be able to walk him to the park, pick him up from preschool or chase him around the backyard while he learns to ride a bike.

'What a pain it is to have Nanny on wheels,' Bev says to her grandson as he sits perched on the armrest of her wheelchair, giggling.

Unlike the other survivors, Bev knew almost instantly after the quake that it was unlikely she would ever walk again. She had a clinical understanding of her injuries from working as a nurse for 30 years and she tackled her recovery with a fierce determination. Rather than dwelling on all that was lost, Bev was level-headed as she looked toward her future as a paraplegic and quickly began mastering the art of the wheelchair.

Two years on, she has returned to work five days a week as a phone triage nurse, she volunteers at a youth health centre, continues to do charity work and babysits her grandson.

Bev's acceptance of the hand she has been dealt is inspiring. Sitting

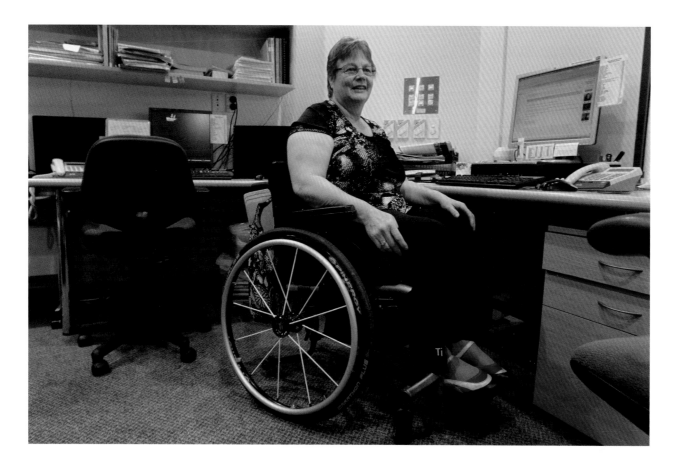

Nurse Bev Edwards was paralysed when the roof of a Sydenham cafe in which she was having lunch collapsed during the February 22, 2011 quake. She is back at work at the Barrington Medical Centre.

**DEAN KOZANIC**

in her Cashmere home, talking while she sews together a fluffy bear for a children's charity, she speaks of just how much her life has changed. The hallways of her dream home have been widened to fit a wheelchair, an elevator has been installed to the first storey, the bathroom had to be transformed into a paraplegic-modified 'wet room', and a new dining room table, tall enough for her to fit her legs under, now sits in the lounge.

Amid a steady stream of teenagers and a rowdy grandson demanding attention, Bev exposes the fears, frustrations and embarrassments of her new life. She now has to cope with the loss of control of her bowel and bladder, she has to swallow a handful of pills every day and she needs strangers to help her reach for groceries in the supermarket.

Bev has crash-landed out of her wheelchair a number of times in public, and the once formidable mother is now at the mercy of passers-by to get back up. She still lives in chronic pain and wakes up regularly throughout the night sobbing.

'It's not all about moaning and groaning but there are some things people just don't realise,' she said. Little things such as folding the washing but not being able to put it away, or having to ring a restaurant in advance to pre-warn them she is in a wheelchair are now regular parts of her new life.

*'There's a lot these people have given up to look after me and they don't get allowances to do that.'*

Bev is not ashamed to admit mourning for the past, but her grief is largely selfless. She believes her accident has hampered her ability to help people effectively as a nurse and she feels guilty that her 17-year-old daughter dropped out of school because she lost the mother she had depended on. And she grieves for her former relationship with her husband, when he was her lover rather than a much-needed best friend.

'There's a lot these people have given up to look after me and they don't get allowances to do that.

'The effects on the families have not been acknowledged enough, nor have they received enough support through their own grief and loss in the past two years,' she says. Bev outlines her grudges and growing concerns for the future.

But, for now, the dark thoughts are quickly shaken off. Poppet, her Jack Russell terrier, pads up to her wheelchair, dumps a well-bitten blue ball half a metre in front of her feet, and Bev loses her train of thought.

She may no longer be able to walk Poppet, but she has created a new paraplegic-friendly version of fetch. Using a metre-long stick, she hooks the ball through a small hole and tosses it past her grandson into the next room as she continues to talk.

'The thing with me now is I can't bear to waste time. I hate sleeping because it's such a waste of time and I resent the fact that you have to sleep because I could be doing so many other things. I feel like I've lost a year out of my life and I just want to catch up.'

Bev Edwards

# THE BEREAVED

**DEATH IS COMMONPLACE.** And usually the grief of the bereaved is private. There is time to sit with the body and say goodbye. But that was not the reality for the 185 families left behind after February 22. Their grief was not their own. Amid the chaos and calamity, their privacy was lost and their pain was on display.

In the direct aftermath, they were forced to play a cruel waiting game. Countless unanswered calls to loved ones' cellphones, long hours in the rain outside collapsed buildings, desperate searches through a frenzied hospital and lonely nights at home waiting for confirmation. The bodies of the victims were pulled from the rubble and quickly hustled out to a temporary morgue for formal identification, not to be returned to the families for weeks. Grieving children had to provide mouth swabs and strands of hair for DNA testing. Information was scarce and a sense of isolation hung over the city. All the while, media were circling.

As time wore on and reality dawned, grief began to slink into their days. Some stopped eating; many were too afraid to sleep. These people may not have been injured or maimed in the disaster but their scars are ugly and deep, their blood is sad and, like those crippled, they too have been changed for life.

There was the widow who fell to her knees when she saw her brother-in-law's face through the glass door. The daughter who cleaned the blood and stones from her father's broken body and refused to let go of his hand. Or the husband who was seen screaming his wife's name before he dragged her body from the rubble of their fish and chip shop.

These people will forever carry the moniker of the dead. Their names are etched into the history of New Zealand and their loved one's memory has been seized by a national tragedy. It has been more than two years since the February 22 quake and the time has not passed easily. The families have lived in a world filled with reminders: broken buildings, ongoing media coverage, public inquiries, coroners' inquests and relentless aftershocks.

For some, Christchurch is little more than the city that stole their loved one. It is unlikely parents of the 68 international students who perished will ever return, and a number of Christchurch families have fled in the past two years because they no longer felt at home. Grief is personal, it lurks within the soul, and for some the loss has been accepted and boxed away. But, for others, time has done little to numb the pain.

Bereaved father David Beaumont still loses his words, his grief is so raw. The 74-year-old feels part of him died along with his only son on

February 22. With free-falling tears, he explains how he has struggled to cope with outliving his adopted child by more than 40 years.

'I would willingly give every day of my life for him,' he says, clutching a damp blue hanky in his fist and pressing it against the side of his quivering mouth.

Matt Beaumont, 31, was a programme scheduler and television host at CTV. He was engaged at the time of his death. Photographs of Matt are attached by magnets to the fridge of his parents' home. Pictures of his carefree, smiling face are soberingly juxtaposed with the harsh reality that he is gone.

Every morning David walks into the lounge, gives his favourite photo the thumbs up, and says: 'Gidday boy.' He may not have seen Matt in two years, but he still speaks of him as though he is alive.

'He is always going to be part of our life and he is never going to fade away.'

It took 98 days for Matt's remains to be identified. The recovered fragments of his body were cremated and sealed in a wooden box. That box now leads a transient lifestyle, moving between Matt's parents, his fiancée and a number of his close friends. Although Matt has a memorial plaque in Avonhead Cemetery, David believes his son is 'quite happy floating around the place'.

Since the death of his son, David has lost his own enthusiasm for life. He stopped playing golf because Matt used to email him after every game and he could not face waiting for an email that was never going to come. As a parent, he believes he lived through his son's life and now sees his own future foreshortened.

'Your children's future is your future, and part of me and my future died on February 22.'

David can no longer bring himself to walk into the Avonhead house Matt and his fiancée shared after he saw his son's guitar casually leaning against the wall in the lounge, abandoned.

'I knew he was learning to play and I saw his guitar leaning against the wall and I could just imagine him putting it down the night before, never to pick it up again.' He chews the side of his finger as he relives the moment. 'I had to leave the house and I can never go back.'

Grief has largely taken over his life and he swallows hard as he admits time has been no great healer. The pain has not waned in the past two years. Christmas Day and birthdays have lost their

significance and become merely 24 hours that hurt a little bit more.

'All I would say is it is never going to be in our past, it is always going to be part of our future. There will never be closure. You can't have closure and you don't want closure because you always live with the memories.'

He sobs as he looks at photos of his son and speaks of the impact of his death.

'I thought I could talk about this but it is still raw as ever. Sometimes I just need to be by myself to pull myself together.'

The pain still chokes David's words and sits heavy on his tongue, but for other bereaved families the grief has retreated with time.

When Jessie Didham's mummy didn't come home, she pined for her every night. Now, tears for the five-year-old's dead mother fall only sporadically, when she remembers. Jessie's father, Mike Didham, 45, brushes her hair on a stool in the lounge as he explains that his family's life has moved on and there is 'nothing to be gained' by longing for the past. He has packaged his grief up into a box and, pointing just above his head, he says the pain is 'just sitting there but you don't have to open it'.

'It's a bloke thing, it's just black and white.'

Mike is now a widower and the solo parent of Jessie and 10-year-old Madison. The successful project manager's 'perfect life' shattered on February 22 when his wife of almost 13 years, Jo Didham, died in the CTV building. He gave himself one night to cry.

After he saw the destroyed building, with his daughters safely at their grandparents' house, Mike came home alone, sat on the couch and cried, thinking: 'What the hell am I going to do? How can I do this without her?' He knew he had no choice but to cope, to move on and to start a new life, because he had two little girls waiting for him.

'The next day the girls got up, they still needed feeding in the morning and to brush their teeth at night. That doesn't change when someone dies.'

Mike's life has turned on its head since the quake. He is now a stay-at-home dad who takes his 10-year-old daughter's class for spelling lessons in the morning, washes and irons a never-ending pile of uniforms during the day and cooks dinner at night.

'I was as blokey as a bloke can get and now I pick the girls up from school and find myself talking to the ladies while we wait and I have an opinion on things like cleaning products and how much Napisan to use in a clothes wash,' he says, laughing.

His wife's life insurance has helped relieve the financial pressure and Mike is grateful for the rare opportunity to play such a key role in his

Now a widower and solo parent of 10-year-old Madison, left, and five-year-old Jessie, Mike Didham has set up a group of friends' wives, called 'the aunties', to help him with any 'girl problems' he needs to deal with in the future.

DEAN KOZANIC

daughters' lives, including acting as father help on school outings.

'Maddie is almost 10 and in five to six years Dad is not going to be that cool any more. It is such a relatively short time to have with these girls that that is everything. This is my life for the rest of it, to be there for them.'

Inside, Mike is still 'sadder than Mr Sad' over the loss of the woman he believes was his soulmate. He is still in love with his wife, feels he will never be able to replace her, and has decided not to complicate the family dynamic by dating again.

'Going to bed by yourself and dealing with everything by yourself is lonely, but it is a sacrifice I need to make for my girls.'

Raising the two on his own is a daunting prospect and Mike has already faced a few hurdles, such as mastering the art of ironing pleated uniforms, giving advice on friendship problems and learning about pop singer Katy Perry. So far, he has not had to 'get my grumpy voice out' very often, but he believes that will change as the pair grow into teenagers.

Mike has established a group of his friends' wives, called 'the aunties', who will be there to answer any 'girl problems' in the future. He has also bought himself a 'fathers raising daughters' book to try and pick up some tips.

'My only reservation about being a solo dad is if I make them too hard. I'm a bloke and if they get hurt, I give them a cuddle and then say "Suck it up". But, I suppose, making them harder isn't necessarily a bad thing — especially when it comes to the boys.'

Mike believes his wife would be proud of how he has coped so far. There are photographs of her all around the house and, not wanting his daughters to forget, he still speaks of her regularly. Often when he struggles to get Jessie to bed at night he says: 'Mum is waiting for you to get to sleep; she's watching you and she's waiting.'

For Mike, the measure of his life now rests on his daughters and the people they grow up to become.

'It doesn't matter how big our house is, that means nothing. The whole thing is the girls and I will sacrifice everything for that.'

# THE WRETCHED

**NOT EVERYONE WHOSE** life was altered by the Christchurch earthquake lost a loved one or would even consider themselves a survivor. Some simply watched the fabric of their lives shred as the city fell. Grief crawled through the streets in the wake of the quake, slipping unnoticed into thousands of ordinary households.

Christchurch's broken heart was evacuated, cordoned off and left to lick its wounds alone in the dark. Power was cut across the city. There was an immediate reduction of services, forcing people to queue for water and use portaloos on street corners. Churches and community centres crumbled into the dirt. Suburbs were isolated and swamped in silt. Every day people lost their homes, their livelihoods and their peace of mind.

Prime Minister John Key labelled February 22, 2011 New Zealand's darkest day, and two years on there are parts of the city where the light is yet to touch. In the aftermath of the quake, a sense of humanity rose from the ashes. Businessmen in suits scoured fallen buildings searching for life, strangers ran injured children to the hospital, and Urban Search and Rescue workers received a poignant and prolonged standing ovation at the Christchurch earthquake memorial service. Neighbourhoods held weekly barbecues, strangers took in the homeless, thousands of students shovelled silt from backyards and residents baked for soldiers manning the cordon.

We rejoiced in our survival and we celebrated our resilience. But it didn't take long for the party to end. The reality of post-disaster life quickly dawned on the city as the government swooped in to restore control. It earmarked hundreds of buildings for demolition and reduced Christchurch to a colour-coded map, red-zoning and effectively wiping out about 8000

homes. Working with unparalleled power, the government's centralised approach belittled local authority and overrode the Christchurch City Council's community-based recovery plan.

The loss of democracy caused anger and fear to fester in the city's grass-roots communities. Insurance woes, Earthquake Commission frustrations, ongoing aftershocks, damaged roads, traffic jams, the loss of a city centre and social scene, skyrocketing rental prices and uncertainty about the future compounded into a potent cocktail for strained, weary Cantabrians. Protesters have hit the streets more than 30 times in the past two years, some protests attracting crowds of up to 4000, to rail against a loss of democracy, council salaries, school closures and the powers of earthquake agencies.

Antisocial behaviour, aggression, domestic violence, alcohol addiction and depression began to take hold of the Garden City. Even the most stoic Cantabrians were not immune, with businessmen turning to anger management classes and people who had never been in trouble with the law appearing before the courts.

The City Mission saw a 100 per cent increase in demand at its foodbank and people who would once have donated or volunteered were seen queuing for help. Women's refuge centres reported daily calls from at-risk women pleading to be rehomed. Police reported an alarming rise in family violence and the Family Court saw Christchurch couples divorce by the bucketload.

Rental rises in the city surged to an eight-and-a-half-year high as the quake-struck rental market ballooned and displaced red-zoners and overseas rebuild workers sought accommodation. A raft of agencies, experts and MPs declared the city was in the midst of a housing crisis and stories of families unlawfully overcrowding houses, sleeping in cars and garages and moving into the abandoned red zone began to surface.

But amid the anger, frustration and uncertainty, green shoots have begun to emerge from the dust. The community has been nurturing them carefully. People have begun to appreciate the scale of the opportunities before them, and different initiatives and ingenious community-based projects have sprung up around the city.

The Gap Filler group has been transforming vacant sites into community spaces since the February quake, including a music venue made from 3000 recycled wooden pallets, a community chess board and an old fridge full of used books for people to exchange. The Re:Start shipping container mall has encouraged thousands of people to return to the abandoned city centre.

The suburb of Addington has grown into a lively hub with its own nightlife and funky cafes. The new Court Theatre, known as The Shed, was built inside a former granary in Addington and has become a cultural landmark in the city's recovery. Shipping containers strewn around seaside

suburbs have been decorated. And thousands of road cones littering the city streets were adorned with flowers on the first anniversary of the quake, to remember those we lost and to show our hope for the future — an act that spread across the world and saw people placing flowers in road cones from Singapore to London.

Christchurch's new identity is blossoming and it has already gained global recognition. The city was awarded the sixth spot in *Lonely Planet*'s Best in Travel top 10 cities for 2013, for the way it was 'bouncing back with a new energy and inventiveness'. The government's plans for the new city centre have also been well received and promise a fresh start, Christchurch's booming construction trade is driving economic recovery both locally and nationally, and thousands of immigrants are expected to flood in for the rebuild over the coming years.

The demolition phase will soon be drawing to an end, and an era of positivity and promise lies ahead.

**THE HUMAN TOLL** of a natural disaster cannot be measured. Suffering and heartache cannot be quantified. Christchurch will always have scars to bear and there is no denying we have grief.

How could we not? We ran from our homes. We cried on the streets. We bled in the rubble. We harbour pain, anger and resentment for what happened to our city, to our people. But Christchurch will be reborn — and the beast that is grief will be repelled by our hope. ■

# DEMOGRAPHY
## THE LOSS OF HISTORY

*Charlie Gates*

The Canterbury earthquakes changed the face of suburban
Christchurch, causing enormous damage to hundreds of hectares
of eastern suburbia, where riverside land slumped dramatically.
Huge forces reshaped the map in a matter of seconds. Whole
suburbs were flooded and buried in tonnes of silt, knee-deep in
places, roads were left twisted and buckled, thousands of homes
were warped and smashed, and power poles were left leaning
precariously.

**THE HUMAN IMPACT** of the earthquakes and the recovery decisions that followed has been profound. Thousands of people have been displaced from their homes and a large slice of Christchurch's history will be lost forever. Some people are leaving homes where their family history stretches back four generations, while elderly residents are leaving the suburbs that have defined their lives — the places where they grew up, married, brought up families and retired. People traumatised by the earthquakes have now had to cope with losing their homes and their communities.

Just over a year after the February quake, the government decided large stretches of suburban land could not be economically repaired. The Canterbury Earthquake Recovery Authority (CERA) announced in June 2011 that 5000 properties would be 'red-zoned', meaning the government would buy the house and land, or just the land, at the most recent rating valuation. The new red zone slowly expanded as CERA declared more suburbs to be beyond economic repair. By late 2012 the process was over and about 8000 homes had been red-zoned across 630 hectares of land.

It is hard to grasp the size of the residential red zone. You can drive for ages and still be inside its borders. It is about four times the size of Hagley Park. It includes a stretch of suburbia that follows the Avon River from the city to the sea, hundreds of homes in the Port Hills made uninhabitable by the risk of rockfall, and pockets of homes in Kaiapoi, Pines Beach and Brooklands.

As the residential red zone has emptied of people, some trees, plants and wildlife have flourished, including these cabbage trees (and others) at 275 River Rd.
**KIRK HARGREAVES**

There is not yet a clear plan for the future of this damaged land, although many community activists are pushing for some of it to be transformed into a riverside park stretching from the heart of the city to the beach. The homes are being demolished as each landowner settles with the government and moves out. Only about 1200 of the nearly 8000 red-zone homes have been demolished so far, with clearance expected to accelerate in 2013. The demolition process could take up to a decade.

The Cammocks are one family with deep roots in the residential red zone. Peter and Liz Cammock lived with two of their four children in a typical 1930s wooden villa in the idyllic riverside suburb of Richmond. The property had provided a home for the Cammock family over four generations going back to the early 1930s. But the February quake changed everything.

Liz was in the Canterbury Television building on the day of the quake. She was one of the few people to survive the building's collapse. 'It was all lost in seconds. When I came down in the CTV building it was 10 seconds. That is how fast my life changed.'

After the quake Liz was reunited with her husband Peter in Latimer Square. They walked back to their Richmond home together and immediately realised their community had been destroyed.

'When we walked along River Road it felt like something had died. This area had died. I felt huge relief to be home, but when I walked through the

door it just felt dead. I can't explain it. It just felt dead and cold and empty,' Liz said.

The home was red-zoned in June 2011.

'When I got out of the CTV building I thought all of Christchurch was flattened. I just thought there were going to be dead bodies everywhere. Is my husband alive? Is my daughter alive? It was really traumatic.

'To lose the house on top of that . . . We have so many wonderful stories around that house — weddings and birthdays. There is a rich narrative around that house for us. It can't be replaced. You just have to let it go. There is a lot of grieving that goes into that.'

For Peter it was the end of the riverside neighbourhood where he grew up and of a home that was bought by his great-uncle in the late 1930s. His great-grandparents lived there, his grandmother lived there, he and his two siblings were raised there and his parents lived and died there. Peter returned to the house in 2008 with Liz and two of their four children to refurbish the place and retire in his old neighbourhood.

'I felt very settled. There was an incredible sense of community. It was like coming home. It was a real sense of homecoming. We would have retired here.'

The quake ended those dreams and marked the fall of a suburb full of his childhood memories. He remembers how his father's Austin 7 car was small enough to drive across the Medway footbridge. He remembers the vegetable gardens, orchards and glasshouses that were slowly replaced by new homes. He remembers his excitement as a child when cars would lose control and end up in the river. He remembers the family marriages in the back garden.

But soon the homes that line both sides of the river in Richmond will all be gone.

'I grew up here with my great-grandparents, my grandmother, my parents and us. All those generations have been taken away. The whole place will be gone. These were the places where we played. This is a whole community that has gone.'

In the nearby suburb of Dallington, 82-year-old Janice Moss has left her family home. The house where she raised her family has now been demolished and soon the Christchurch community that has defined her will be largely wiped from the map.

Janice is a daughter of Dallington. It is the suburb where she played as a child, married, worked, raised a family and grew fruit trees from saplings. A large expanse of the suburb has been red-zoned, from the loop in the Avon River in the south to New Brighton Road in the north. Her family home in Gayhurst Road, where she lived for almost 60 years and raised four daughters, was also red-zoned in June 2011. She did not want to leave her family home, and tried to avoid the area while it was being demolished.

**TOP** The twisted footbridge across the Avon River at Medway St was originally warped in the September 4, 2010 quake. Residents experienced sadness and relief when the Richmond bridge was removed in February 2013 for storage at Ferrymead Heritage Park before a permanent home can be found for it as a quake memorial.
**DEAN KOZANIC**

**BOTTOM** The bridge over the Avon between Avonside Dr and River Rd was deemed beyond repair.
**DEAN KOZANIC**

'We lived in that house for 59 years. I would still be there, but it is not there now. I knew every inch of it. I didn't want to see it come down. Deep down, it does affect you.

'Looking back on it now, I was extremely frightened to be put into the red zone from the word go. It was strange leaving. It was tough.

'We can only live one day at a time.'

Janice was born at the family home just across the river from Dallington in Avonside Drive. Her great-grandparents came from England in 1864 and established the farm in Avonside Drive, where she was raised. 'I really do go back an awfully long way.'

She remembers a semi-rural childhood playing in what were then fields, farms and orchards.

'It has been a wonderful area to live in. There were a lot of orchards down the road. The boys used to play down there. At Porritt Park there was a farm with racehorses. There were huge great trees across Gayhurst Road. There was no road on the north side of the river.

'Avonside Drive only went so far. It was just a track. Gayhurst Road didn't reach McBratneys Road; there was a poultry farm there.'

Janice met her future husband at the local Sunday school when she was four and he was six. Wallace Moss, who died 20 years ago, came from Lionel Street, just around the corner from her family house. They were married in 1953, as soon as Janice's parents allowed.

'My mother and father said I had to be 23 before I could get married. So when I was 23 years and one day old I got married.'

The newlyweds moved into their new home in Gayhurst Road — it was where Janice would stay until the whole street was red-zoned in mid-2011. She worked at the Dallington playcentre and a local high school, looking after the children of teachers while they were working. She still sees some of the children she looked after when she is out and about in Dallington.

'I am walking down the road and I see one of the kids I had at that time and they call out "Mossy".'

Even after her four daughters moved away and her husband died, the Gayhurst Road house remained a gathering place for the family — a place where Janice could catch up with her eight grandchildren and three great-grandchildren. She has now moved to a small bungalow in Burwood, but managed to rescue a few trees and even some compost from her old garden.

'I couldn't move the lemon tree, which was a shame as it was 50 years old.' The raspberry bushes also had to remain. She remembers what became of the raspberries with a proud smile. 'I stopped by the house one day and asked the demolition worker what happened to the raspberries. He said they had eaten every single one and they were beautiful.'

Janice remembers when her Christchurch

**TOP** Janice Moss was born at the family home in Avonside Dr and lived in Gayhurst Rd after she was married in 1953 until her street was red-zoned in mid-2011.

**CARYS MONTEATH**

**BOTTOM** Janice Moss takes another look at the family photos from earlier days living near the Avon River. Her brick house was demolished in July 2012.

**CARYS MONTEATH**

suburb was largely fields. Now she will see the neighbourhood she has lived in for eight decades return to that state.

**IN JULY 2012,** a modest brick house on the banks of the Avon River was demolished. It was one of thousands that will be cleared in the residential red zone over the next decade, slowly transforming these once proud suburbs back into their original fields. Exploring the family history of a single red-zone house reveals much about the deep emotional roots people have in these doomed suburbs. When demolition workers arrived at one Dallington home to begin work, they found a chalk message scrawled on the wall. The message read:

> To the Coopers — Melva, Bill, Steven, Vicki, Wendy, Tammy and Kelly.
> Memories of wonderful neighbours, lifelong friendships and childhood memories in this home.
> Playing with the Coopers, feeding the ducks and picnics in the park.
> What wonderful brickwork Bill did!
> He conquered Mother Nature.
> Love, Julie and the Bryson family.

This simple farewell message was written as a tribute to a family's 50-year history in the home. It's a history that begins in 1957 with a bricklayer called Bill Cooper, who built the house that provided a home for his family for more than half a century. When he died in 1968, the house became a way for his family to remember him. It was a point of family pride that his brickwork survived the quakes intact.

Bill's wife, Melva, lived there until 2005 and his three children, Steven, Vicki and Wendy, remember an idyllic childhood in the riverside home. The demolition of the house was a sad moment for Steven.

'My father built the place and his life was cut short before he had a chance to enjoy what he made. That house was the last tangible reminder of his life. It was still there and it was still his.

'He took a lot of pride in his work. As a boy, I remember he would point

A poignant message left on the bricks of what was for many years the Cooper family home in Locksley Ave, Dallington. It was built by bricklayer Bill Cooper in 1957 and demolished in July 2012.
**KIRK HARGREAVES**

**TOP** The foundations of the house at 239 Locksley Ave under construction around 1957.
**PHOTO SUPPLIED**

**MIDDLE** Dallington bricklayer Bill Cooper with his son Steven on the sunny northern patio shortly after the house was finished.
**PHOTO SUPPLIED**

**BOTTOM** By 1964, 239 Locksley Ave was home to the growing Cooper children: Vicki, 8 (left), Wendy, 6, and Steven, 10.
**PHOTO SUPPLIED**

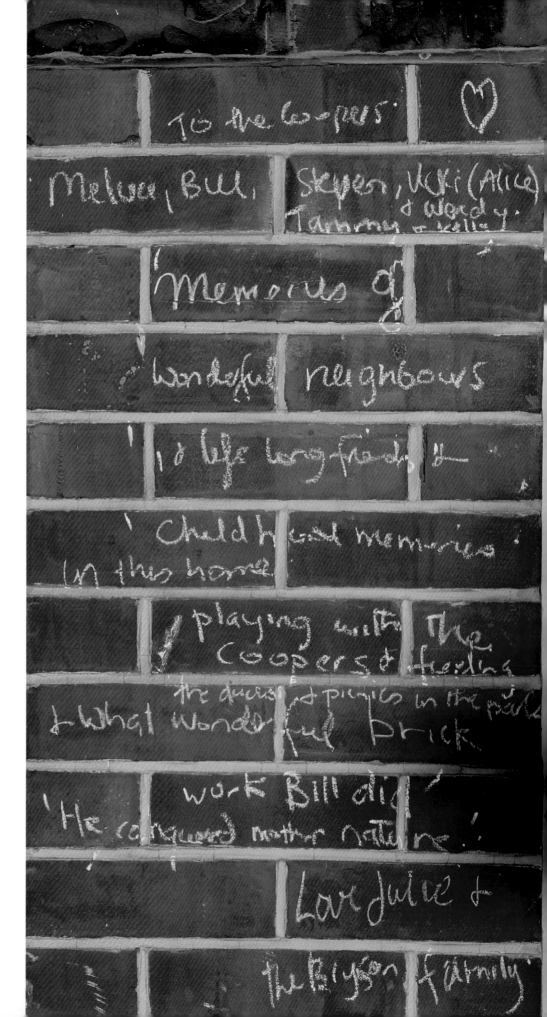

out the places he had built. The house lasted well through the quakes.'

Family photographs show Steven, aged about two, toddling about the construction site as the house is being built. One photograph shows Bill with his arm around his young son on the terrace of the newly completed house. Steven remembers a happy childhood there.

'It is only as I got older and talked to others that I realised how lucky we were. At the back of the house was this big section that we could play in. We would just play there right through the summer.'

Steven's younger sister Wendy was 'born and bred' in the house. She also has fond memories of her childhood in the suburb. 'It was good. There were always local kids hanging out doing things. In those days it was a big, open area where we played hide-and-seek and made a fort.

'It was a nice family home. There is a sadness there for the whole community that has been lost and the spirit of the people that lived there.'

In 2005 Melva moved into a rest home and the house was sold. It changed hands a few times before it was purchased by Mary Jo Gagan in 2010. She didn't know it at the time, but she would be the last person to own this pleasant riverside home.

Mary Jo moved in with her partner in August 2010, just a few weeks before the September quake, and loved her new neighbourhood. The suburb recovered quickly from the first quake, but was very badly hit in February 2011.

'After the September quake, things went back to normal for a while and it was beautiful. Things went to hell in a handbag after February. Our house was more broken. We couldn't use the garage because we couldn't get the door open. After February, we slept under the kitchen table because we were so afraid.'

Living in the red zone was unpleasant, she said.

'We stuck it out, using the portaloo and taking

a shower at the gym. Rental people moved out first and then the home-owners started to drift away. It was kind of scary because my partner travels a lot and many evenings I was there by myself.

'One night the phone was out, so I felt pretty isolated. There were reports of burglaries and arson on our block, so you wanted people to know you were home. It was scary for a woman on her own.'

She moved to Auckland with her partner in March 2012.

'It was hard leaving because it was so beautiful by the river. It was a great neighbourhood. We had good times there. We didn't live there that long, but we had a good time.'

A few months after Mary Jo moved out of the house, Julianne Dobson went on a 'pilgrimage' of the Christchurch streets she remembered from her childhood and knew would soon be gone. When she found the empty house where the Coopers had lived it evoked many childhood memories. She had grown up in the house next door and remembers playing with the Cooper children. Wanting to honour those memories, she wrote her personal message on the wall of the Coopers' house in chalk. It seemed fitting it was on the very bricks Bill Cooper had so carefully put into place all those decades ago.

'I went around places I knew from my childhood in Christchurch. I couldn't believe it. Everyone has left. It was like an empty shell.

'Our old house is standing there majestically and held up well. These houses just stand there empty, but they are full of lots of memories from years ago. It made me feel sad because most of my old neighbourhood has gone now.

'It was my way of saying goodbye to the area myself and recognising the souls of the houses and how well they did against Mother Nature. There is a great sadness there, but some wonderful, wonderful memories of life by the river.'

*'It was my way of saying goodbye to the area myself and recognising the souls of the houses and how well they did against Mother Nature. There is a great sadness there, but some wonderful, wonderful memories of life by the river.'*

Just weeks after she wrote her message, the demolition crew arrived to demolish the house. A team from City Salvage was contracted by construction company Hawkins to do the job. Hawkins itself is contracted by insurance company IAG to manage demolition work across Christchurch. Once the job is signed over to City Salvage, the home becomes the company's property. Workers can recover as much material as they think is worth the time.

Over a week, the demolition workers salvaged from the Cooper home internal doors, light fittings, the power board, the carpet, the fitted kitchen, the laundry tub, the bath, the shower, the cupboard doors, the hot-water

City Salvage workers — including Mark (Will) Williamson seen here disposing of tiles — spent a week removing items such as doors, lights, carpets, kitchen and bathroom fittings from the old Cooper home.

**KIRK HARGREAVES**

cylinder and the ceiling insulation. Once the inside was stripped, the tiles and timber were removed from the roof before a digger arrived to pull down the walls and clear the site.

The kitchen, windows and doors sold for $8950 on Trade Me to Barry Ward of Invercargill, who is renovating a house just outside the city for his family.

The ceiling insulation and the hot-water cylinder were sold to Christchurch people.

Gib board, timber and flooring went to the Burwood Recycling Centre, where untreated timber will be sorted and reused and some treated timber shredded and reused. Gib board will be sorted and turned back into wall-boards.

Water pipes went to Bristol Metals, which squashes them and sends them to China.

Some of the metal went to Christchurch foundry AW Fraser, which turns the copper into brass and bronze machine components for items like drilling equipment and even large diggers like the ones that demolish buildings.

Tiles, concrete foundations and the bricks that Bill Cooper mortared into place and held such pride for his family went to hardfill in Lyttelton Harbour as part of a project to 'reclaim' land to redevelop the port.

When the house was demolished in July 2012 *The Press* documented the event, using family photographs of Bill Cooper building the house in 1957 to

form a sequence showing an empty plot becoming a family home and then returning to an empty plot. It is a strange full circle turned over more than five decades.

**THE HISTORY OF** the residential red zone goes back much further than the 1950s, though. The Coopers' home was built in a wave of suburban expansion that spread east down the Avon River in that decade. But the true roots of Christchurch's suburbs can be found further upriver from the Coopers' home, on the edge of the city centre. On a rise overlooking a bend in the river is a small, unassuming house with a wrap-around veranda. It may look like any other Kiwi villa, but it is perhaps the oldest house in the residential red zone and tells the story of Christchurch's settler past.

The former Richmond farmhouse on River Road dates back to the 1870s, but will be demolished as part of the clearance of the suburban red zone. The building has changed very little over more than a century, but the neighbourhood has changed beyond recognition. Once part of a 40-hectare farm that was accessed from Stanmore Road, the villa is now surrounded by houses.

The title for the plot was first sold in 1851. It is unclear exactly when the house was built, but it was bought by the Templer family in 1876, and photographs from the period show them using the home. A nearby street was named after the early settler family.

The house is a key to the history of Christchurch's suburban development. Early suburbs were formed when large farm estates were sold upon the owner's death. The large farms were typically divided into quarter-acre sections for housing. A series of large farms stretching east along the Avon River from Fitzgerald Avenue were

**TOP** The back of the Cooper house under construction in 1957.
**PHOTO SUPPLIED**

**MIDDLE TOP** Melva Cooper and Kelly the cat outside 239 Locksley Ave in April 1980.
**PHOTO SUPPLIED**

**MIDDLE BOTTOM** The diggers move in to pull down the walls of the Coopers' home in mid-winter 2012.
**DAVID HALLETT**

**BOTTOM** The section at 239 Locksley Ave slowly returns to how it was before Bill Cooper started work on the home in 1957.
**KIRK HARGREAVES**

**RIGHT** The former Richmond farmhouse on River Rd is believed to be the oldest home in Christchurch's residential red zone, but is scheduled for demolition along with many others.
**KIRK HARGREAVES**

divided in the early 20th century and became new suburbs.

The historic home on River Road was bought by John Walter in 1985. He was in the house when the September 2010 earthquake hit. An engineer, he had anticipated his historic home would not perform well in a quake. He leapt into a bay window a matter of seconds after the earthquake struck at 4.35am. Moments later, about 20 kilograms of plaster fell on the pillow where his head had been. The house is beyond repair.

'Some of the brick walls collapsed. It is fairly shattered. The house is a write-off. There is damage on damage. It used to be beautiful.'

The building appears simple from River Road, but the back of the house, which was formerly the arrival point, features neo-Gothic windows and a long veranda. Another feature, a set of elaborate folding-panel doors in a curving archway, still worked before the quakes.

John Walter described the folding doors as a remnant of the home's past. 'I think they used to do a lot of entertaining here. The doors could fold back so you could create a large dance space.'

Members of the Templer family would occasionally visit the home, he said. 'I think they think of it as the family home.'

He hopes a large totara tree on the property will remain to mark where the historic home stood. 'I want to be able to find the place in the future.'

Once the houses are cleared and services have been decommissioned, the trees will be the only reminder of many Christchurch suburbs. The residential red zone is home to hundreds of mature trees lining the Avon River and on private land. Some are more than 100 years old. The government has promised the trees will be spared in the demolition of red-zone homes, but Christchurch activists fear they could be accidentally killed.

Avon-Otakaro Network co-chair Evan Smith is concerned about that prospect. 'A tree may be retained during demolition work, but a big mechanical digger going over the roots can kill it.' The network is campaigning for the residential red zone to become a large park for the city. Smith hopes to catalogue trees and vegetation in the residential red zone. Dozens of mature trees have been recorded on an asset register and ecologists are studying the red zone to record significant plant life. An audit of one site near Richmond Park found more than 400 plants.

'There is intrinsic value in saving mature trees from a heritage, community, cultural, botanic and ecological perspective. There is enormous value in these assets and some have been there for over 100 years.

'It is much easier to manage land if it has some tree cover. It stops grasses and weeds from getting out of hand. It is really critical we keep as many as possible.' Smith has seen tree saplings already sprouting on empty red-zone sites.

But flora is not the only part of the natural world that has prospered in the residential red zone. As the area slowly empties of people, wildlife has flourished in their absence. Possums have moved into abandoned Christchurch suburbs and a rare bird has returned to the city. Landcare Research pest control scientist Janine Duckworth said possums would prosper without humans.

'It doesn't surprise me that we are seeing more of them, as they do try and avoid people. With fewer dogs in the area, that will allow them to move into places they may not have been able to take advantage of in the past. If they are less disturbed, then more young possums will grow into adults.'

Richmond resident Rex Collins found a possum 'the size of a fox terrier' on the roof of his home. It is the first he has encountered in 16 years of living in the suburb.

'We woke up in the middle of the night to this loud crashing sound on the roof. We have this problem with squatters next door, so we thought it was someone jumping on our roof. We rang the police and they came pretty quickly. They had a good look around and then they found this huge possum.

'We looked up on the roof and there was this possum staring back at me. He was huge, by far the biggest possum I have ever seen. He was about the size of a fox terrier in body size. He had these huge big round eyes about the size of two-dollar coins.

'A lot of wildlife is coming back into the area. The wildlife is taking over again.'

A very rare Australasian bittern has also returned to Christchurch after an absence of around eight years. There are only 700 such bitterns in New Zealand, but bird enthusiasts have spotted about eight in the wetlands near Bexley at the eastern end of the residential red zone.

*Press* photographer and bird enthusiast David Hallett said the bittern was 'rarer than most kiwis' and said it was 'amazing' the bird had come back.

**THE RESIDENTIAL RED** zone is a unique suburban landscape full of rich social history, new wildlife and deep emotional roots. As 2013 begins, the area is in limbo. It is a twisted and shattered suburban landscape that is not yet demolished nor fully abandoned. The only sounds in the more deserted suburbs are birdsong and the distant hum of machinery slowly unpicking the neighbourhood.

It is bleak. Broken homes sit at strange angles, their fences scarred with tagging. A little row of shops — once a lively bar, a video store and a pizzeria — sit smashed and empty.

*It is bleak. Broken homes sit at strange angles, their fences scarred with tagging. A little row of shops — once a lively bar, a video store and a pizzeria — sit smashed and empty.*

The streets are gap-toothed, with empty sites dominated by large brown puddles the size of boating lakes. At night, there are dark, deserted streets with no lights. There are hollow-eyed houses leaning toward one another like conspirators. There are pockmarked streets covered with puddles and gravel.

There are houses where burglars have stripped out all the windows and fittings. There are homes where departing residents have scattered broken furniture and toys across the front yard. A powerless and angry gesture. Other homes have been broken into and tagged. It is mile after mile of shattered suburbia.

These were once lovely suburbs set around the Avon River. It was the Kiwi dream — a modest, pleasant life that you didn't need to be super-rich to enjoy. Many red-zone residents do not want to leave their homes. They feel powerless, afraid, and sad for everything they have lost. They have strong memories of their life in these suburbs.

Janice Moss remembers the fruit trees she nurtured from saplings in her backyard and the daughters she raised over decades in her home.

Peter Cammock remembers his baby-boomer childhood on the generous

A sense of humour helps. Eastern Christchurch motorists are warned to expect smooth, level roads as they drive further west in the city.

**DEAN KOZANIC**

banks of the Avon. His childhood home and every home on both sides of the river will soon be gone. Whole communities will be cleared.

But the residential red zone could provide a hopeful future for Christchurch. The idea of the land becoming an Avon River park stretching from the city to the sea has gained support in Christchurch from local communities and political figures. Campaigners believe the park would be unique in the world, providing a huge asset for the quake-damaged city and creating a living memorial to what has been lost.

It is an idea that has proved compelling. With the trees intact, people would be able to find the places where they once lived as they walk from the city to the sea. A place rich with history and memories for the people who lived there could point the way for the future of the city.

The residential red zone is a place of memory, history and potential new horizons. ■

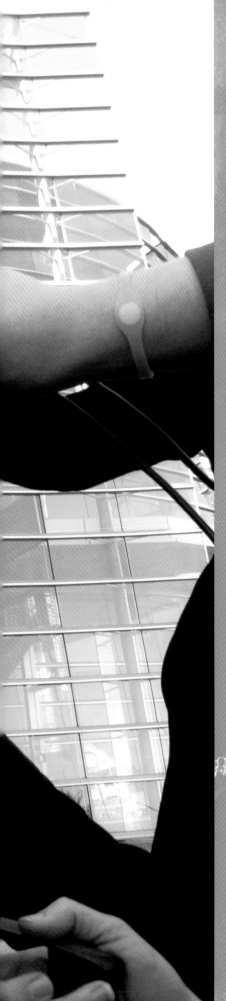

# GOVERNANCE
## THE CHANGING POLITICAL LANDSCAPE

*Lois Cairns*

The Canterbury earthquakes sparked a seismic shake-up of the city's governance arrangements. The first quake struck just five weeks out from the October 2010 local-body elections and instantly changed the political landscape. Before the September 4 quake, Christchurch mayor Bob Parker had been lagging behind in the opinion polls and was facing the prospect of handing over the mayoral chains to his left-leaning opponent, veteran politician Jim Anderton. Popular rumour has it that Anderton joked at the time that only an event of seismic proportions would stop him winning — and he was right.

**WHEN THE EARTH** finally stopped shaking in the pre-dawn hours of September 4, Parker emerged from the dust and the rubble as exactly the kind of leader rattled residents wanted in a crisis — someone calm but authoritative, with unflappable communication skills. Parker's performance in those chaotic days and weeks immediately after the 7.1 magnitude quake was strong enough to propel him back into office and into the centre of a brewing maelstrom of political conflict and personality clashes that would eventually lead him almost to resign.

In the nearly three years since the 2010 elections, the political landscape in Christchurch has changed almost beyond imagination. A new government department, the Canterbury Earthquake Recovery Authority — known more commonly in the city by its acronym, CERA — has taken control of the rebuild and been wielding unprecedented powers. Its dominance in the decision-making process has left many local-body politicians feeling impotent and has raised serious questions about the extent to which Wellington is dictating what happens in Christchurch. On more than one occasion people have taken to the streets to protest against the perceived loss of democracy and to call for power to be returned to those most affected by the quakes — those who call Christchurch home and are invested, emotionally and financially, in its future.

Clashes between Parker's council and CERA's master, the indomitable, unshakeable Gerry Brownlee, Minister for Canterbury Earthquake Recovery,

A grim-faced Mayor Bob Parker fronts up again to media after the city's darkest day, February 22, 2011.
**DAVID HALLETT**

have become increasingly common and have led to many terse exchanges and veiled attacks. At the same time as the council has been faced with an outsider invading its territory, it has almost been ripped apart by internal politicking and power struggles. Many in Christchurch argue that the council has been its own worst enemy; that it has created a rod for its own back — and in many ways it has. But the truth is, the trauma, turbulence and uncertainty of the past two years would have tested the resolve, resilience and cohesion of any local authority.

**IN THE THEATRE** of Christchurch governance, Brownlee is without doubt the puppet-master. He holds all the strings. But in all good theatrical productions a villain and a hero are required, and in Christchurch these roles seem to have fallen on the shoulders of Christchurch City Council chief executive Tony Marryatt and CERA chief executive Roger Sutton respectively. Critics of mayor Bob Parker argue his role is to provide the comic relief.

Controversy is nothing new to Marryatt, who was appointed in 2007 after an 11-year stint as chief executive of the Hamilton City Council. His time in Hamilton included a falling-out with one-term mayor David Braithwaite, who alleged that Marryatt created an 'environment of fear and bullying'.

Marryatt's problems in Christchurch, though, have not been with his

2000-odd employees, most of whom rank him pretty highly, but with the public, with whom he has largely failed to engage. That is because in many ways Marryatt is an old-school public servant who prefers to work behind the scenes. He has never courted publicity and seems to prefer to let others do the talking. But he is a forceful man with a strong wheeler-dealer streak to his personality and a liking for bringing propositions to the council table. Where he often falls down is in convincing the public of the value of those propositions. Before the quakes Marryatt and Parker pushed through a series of major decisions which, one by one, damaged their relationships with many across town.

After the quakes, when people were desperate for leadership, Marryatt was nowhere to be seen. He was not on the six o'clock news, or at public meetings explaining what the council was doing to get the city back on its feet. The public couldn't understand that. He became a target for their anger and their frustration.

While Marryatt is often vilified as being aloof and out of touch, Sutton, as *The Press* put it in an article in 2012, is known as the likeable, bespectacled, long-haired, pinstripe-suited alpha nerd making what many people say is a decent fist of a thankless job.

When it was announced in May 2011 that Sutton, at the time chief executive of lines company Orion New Zealand, would become the new earthquake recovery boss, the public response was favourable, to put it mildly. Former Wigram MP Jim Anderton said it was the best news he had had since the February 2011 quake. Port Hills Labour MP Ruth Dyson gave his appointment '12 out of 10', Canterbury Communities' Earthquake Recovery Network chairman Tom McBrearty was 'delighted' and Canterbury Employers' Chamber of Commerce chief executive Peter Townsend said it was 'the most important government appointment of the year'.

The Saturday before he started in the job, Sutton featured on the cover of the *Weekend Press* 'Your Weekend' magazine in a local adaptation of Shepard Fairey's Barack Obama 'Hope' poster, used during the 2008 US presidential campaign. After months of Civil Defence management, states of emergency and immeasurable heartache, Sutton was seen as a harbinger of change.

Almost unnaturally easy-going, Sutton does not shy away from the media or the public. He loves an audience and happily chats with anyone. Perhaps his biggest problem is that expectations of him have been built uncomfortably high; the only way for him to go in the public's estimation is down. And already there are signs he has fallen, slightly, from grace. In the unfamiliar role of public servant, answerable to Brownlee, Sutton can't just

run CERA his way — a fact that hasn't escaped the public's notice. The Letters to the Editor column in *The Press* frequently features letters from people questioning Sutton's freedom to operate and whether Wellington has hobbled its white charger.

The man many believe is doing the hobbling is, of course, the notoriously combative Brownlee. The former woodwork teacher turned National MP is without doubt the most powerful man in Christchurch. Thanks to the Canterbury Earthquake Recovery Act he can rewrite the laws of the land almost as he sees fit. With a stroke of the pen he can cross out a suburb in one place, mark it down in another. Well, not quite so easily, but on paper never has a minister had such personal responsibility. And Brownlee has not been shy about using his special recovery powers.

He is also not one to mince words. Since the February 22 earthquake Brownlee has regularly launched withering attacks on anyone challenging his version of the recovery. He has called heritage advocates 'misinterpretation specialists', blasted insurers for 'scaremongering', and lambasted owners of TC3 (Technical Category 3) properties in the green zone for their 'carping and moaning'. He has also hit out more than once at Christchurch's mayor, most famously calling him a 'clown' — a remark that almost led Parker to resign. Brownlee also labelled *The Press* the 'enemy of the recovery'.

Parker, while often denigrated by his opponents for being a 'quiz-show host' or a 'show pony', is not a clown. Yes, he's made some misjudgements during his term as mayor, but even his critics don't deny he is an intelligent thinker with a good grasp of issues. And no one doubts that in a crisis he is a master communicator. His work during the earthquakes won him the Public Relations Institute of New Zealand award for Communicator of the Year but Parker, by his own admission, admits that during his time as mayor he has not always communicated as well as he might.

'Although getting messages across to the public should be my stock and trade, I have found it difficult,' he admits in his book *Ripped Apart: A City in Chaos*. 'Communicating directly, during the earthquakes, enabled people to appreciate the person I am. Unfortunately it is difficult to maintain that momentum in normal circumstances.'

Parker says his failure to communicate has at times cost him some key battles; it may yet cost him the mayoralty in 2013.

The aftershocks from the first quake were still rumbling through Christchurch in late 2010 when a new city council was sworn in. The winds of change had seen some long-standing councillors dumped in the October election. Several new faces, some of them closely aligned to the left-leaning People's Choice team who were still smarting over Anderton's failure to wrestle the mayoralty off Parker, were dipping their toes into local-body politics for the first time. They were eager to make their mark and have their voices heard.

Even under normal circumstances bedding in a new council can be a testing process, and the circumstances in Christchurch in October 2010 were far from normal. The council was facing the Herculean task of piecing the city back together and it desperately needed strong leadership and a unified council. It had neither.

While Parker may have provided a uniting voice immediately after the quakes, around the council table he was regarded as something of a polarising character. Councillors talk of how they felt they were pushed into A and B teams. Those in the A team were in Parker's camp and privy to information; those in the B team were on the outer and often kept in the dark about what was going on. It soon became clear that Parker was at the helm of a dysfunctional ship. From where the public was sitting it looked like petty politicking was taking precedence over getting the city back on its feet and the council had lost its way.

That public perception intensified just before Christmas 2011 when it was revealed the council had awarded Marryatt a $68,000 pay rise. In a city where so many people had lost their jobs and their livelihoods because of the quakes, that news went down like a veritable lead balloon and Marryatt, who had never polled highly in the popularity stakes, found himself public enemy number one. People simply could not understand how the council could justify giving Marryatt such a whopping increase when the organisation he headed appeared to be floundering.

A few months earlier, when respected senior city councillor Chrissie Williams suddenly announced she was quitting — citing the dysfunction and lack of leadership in the council as the reason for her departure — serious questions began to be asked about the council's ability to lead the rebuild.

As letters to the editor flowed into *The Press* demanding Marryatt's head roll, the trust between council staff and councillors continued to erode. There were allegations that some councillors were leaking confidential information to the media. As a result of these public disclosures, some staff became concerned that if they discussed confidential or commercially sensitive issues with councillors, the discussion might be made public before matters had been thought through or that such information might be used for political purposes. They became reluctant to share information with elected members and the communication lines between councillors and management began to close. Council meetings became 'strained and negative', Parker notes in his book, and public confidence in the council sank to new lows.

*It was against this backdrop that 4000 people gathered outside the council's Hereford St offices on a midsummer's day in early 2012 to call for a change of leadership . . . The message the public was sending to the council was clear and unequivocal: Lift your game.*

Crisis at the city council. The government brought in Kerry Marshall as a Crown observer due to tensions around the council table and threats by some councillors to resign.

**DEAN KOZANIC**

The council's problems reached a crisis point when another senior city councillor, Sue Wells, threatened to follow Williams' lead and resign. Publicly, she called for the government to appoint a commissioner to replace the whole council. Parker, fearing that if Wells resigned at least one other councillor would follow suit, finally rang Prime Minister John Key and asked for help.

As he recalls in *Ripped Apart*, Parker told the prime minister, 'John, this is the situation I've got. On one side I've got all these guys who are undermining everything . . . On the other side I've got good councillors resigning. They've had a gutsful. They are sick of the tension. They are not enjoying their lives. Their own lives are tough enough. They come into this place and it is just gut-aching stress. You may need to contemplate putting commissioners into this place because if I lose these councillors, we've lost the council. It will not be able to function in the best interests of the city and support central government and the needs of the city.'

The government responded immediately by appointing former Nelson mayor Kerry Marshall as a Crown observer to monitor the council and help it address governance issues. At the same time Brownlee, worried by a draft report from the Department of Building and Housing criticising the council's handling of building consents, thundered a five-page letter of expectations to Christchurch city councillors. He reminded them the Crown had an unusual degree of interest in the rebuild and its tolerance for shenanigans was wearing very, very thin.

It was against this backdrop that 4000 people gathered outside the council's Hereford St offices on a midsummer's day in early 2012 to call for a change of leadership. Marryatt's controversial $68,000 pay rise was the lightning rod for their anger and frustration but at the heart of the protest was concern at the slow progress of the city's rebuild. The message the public was sending to the council was clear and unequivocal: Lift your game.

It is interesting to note that a public backlash against bureaucracy is a common feature in post-disaster situations. The causes of the backlash are almost always the same — lack of meaningful community engagement, decisions being made behind closed doors, poor communication, divided

accountabilities, poor governance arrangements and lack of leadership. Labour's earthquake recovery spokeswoman Lianne Dalziel believes that holds true in Christchurch, and the government must take at least some of the blame. She argues the CERA model hasn't provided the city with the leadership it requires.

'It was supposed to be a small agency supporting the coordination of the recovery effort. It has grown into a large government department that continues to fail to communicate with affected residents. What we need is for central government, local government, the community and the developers to be fully engaged in goal setting and integrated strategic planning. It is not just the council that needs to step up to the plate now.'

Under Marshall's stewardship the council did institute change — a charter committing councillors to the good governance of Christchurch has been signed and a new code of conduct drawn up. It is progress, but as anyone observing a council meeting can attest, a level of distrust lingers. That is unlikely to change until there is a new mix around the council table.

**CERA'S USURPING OF** the council's traditional decision-making roles is perhaps most clearly illustrated in the drawing-up of plans for the rebuilding of Christchurch's CBD.

The dust clouds from buildings felled by the February 22 quakes had barely settled on the ground when it became clear a major rebuild of the CBD

was on the cards. Within the four avenues there was devastation at every turn, and as the days and weeks went by the number of buildings slated for demolition in the city's deserted CBD crept steadily upward. The scale of the destruction meant there was never going to be a quick-fix for Christchurch's broken centre; there was too much damage over too big an area for Band-Aids to be applied. A bold plan was needed for a new city centre that was better — if not bigger — than the one that was there before.

Within 10 weeks of the February earthquake the Christchurch City Council had launched a public engagement campaign aimed at maximising community involvement in drawing up that plan. And the public responded in unprecedented numbers, with young and old, near and far, logging on to council-run websites and social media to share their ideas. A two-day expo in May 2011 attracted more than 10,000 residents, and by the end of the six-week consultation period the council had amassed more than 106,000 suggestions from the public about what they wanted to see in the CBD.

Armed with the public's wish list, the council set about turning their aspirations into a working document that would guide the city centre's redevelopment over the next 10 to 20 years. After months of work the council unanimously adopted its draft Central City Plan and unveiled to the public its vision for a low-rise, compact CBD filled with parks and open spaces. They costed the plan at about $2 billion and boldly included proposals for light rail and a raft of state-of-the-art facilities including a metropolitan sports facility and a new swimming centre. They outlined

plans for specialised precincts and a network of lanes that would make it easy for people to move around.

After a further period of consultation the council signed off the plan and handed it over to Brownlee. It would be his call whether the plan became operative or was placed on a shelf to gather dust. As demolition crews continued the laborious process of pulling down the shattered remains of the CBD, news on the rebuild front went quiet. Brownlee was still pondering. He finally broke his silence in April 2012 when he announced he was handing control of the city centre rebuild to a new unit within CERA — the Christchurch Central Development Unit (CCDU) — headed by former Timaru City Council chief executive Warwick Isaacs.

Brownlee's move to set up the CCDU was interpreted by many as another slap in the face for the council, a vote of no-confidence in its ability to lead the rebuild, but Brownlee went out of his way to heap praise on the council for the work it had done.

'When you have a good idea, which the draft plan is, you need a vehicle that can deliver the required result in the most cohesive and efficient manner,' Brownlee told media at the time. The CCDU was the best placed to do that; the best placed to give the plan life.

Parker was at Brownlee's side during the press conference and outwardly seemed to accept the government's intervention. He put a brave face on the announcement, claiming the council had always known that central government would step in and take control. But privately he was seething. In *Ripped Apart* Parker speaks candidly of the disappointment the council felt at being sidelined again: 'Now after all the work we had done with our community, we were again reminded of our relative impotence in our own city. The CCDU's task, as much as we tried to rationalise it, made us feel that we were, again, being pushed to one side. The message seemed to be: "nice try guys, but now the real team is going to finish the task".'

In their press releases Brownlee and Parker spoke of the CCDU and the council working in partnership, but this was a fallacy. Some key council staff were seconded to the CCDU but they had to sign confidentiality agreements which effectively meant they could talk to no one outside the unit about what they were working on. The council, for the most part, was in the dark about what the CCDU was up to.

Tellingly, it was not until almost 70 days into the CCDU's process that Parker received his first glimpse of their work. When councillors were eventually briefed on the CCDU's plan — five days before the scheduled public unveiling — they were shocked to learn the government's ambitious plan for the CBD came with a $1 billion funding gap that it expected the council to fill. Only some fast talking by Brownlee and assurances that the

funding gap would close stopped the council from withdrawing its support for the plan.

Just how much that funding gap closes will only become clear as the plan moves into the execution phase and individual projects are scoped and costed. But already there are signs of conflict ahead. The government's wish list of projects is big and the council's coffers small. It won't be able to afford to pay for everything the government expects without either borrowing heavily, burdening ratepayers with hefty rate rises, or selling off some of its silver — all things it is reluctant to do. With the government reluctant to compromise on its vision for the CBD and the council unwilling or unable to pay for it all, further tension and conflict are inevitable. The question is, how far can the council push before the government pushes back? And with what consequences?

**THE BIRTH OF** a new government department to lead the rebuild has inevitably given rise to concerns about what role the local community plays in decision-making. Many are concerned that too many decisions about Christchurch are being made in Wellington and the voice of the community has been muted by the Canterbury Earthquake Recovery Act.

Those concerns were heightened in 2012 when the government announced it was not going to deliver on its promise to hold democratic elections for Environment Canterbury in 2013. At the urging of some Canterbury mayors the government had stepped in and sacked ECan councillors early in 2010, replacing them with commissioners, because of concerns that internal conflicts were stopping the regional council from

CCDU director Warwick Isaacs stands by the Avon River, the redevelopment of which will be one of the keystone projects in the central city blueprint.
**DON SCOTT**

making progress on key issues. It passed legislation at the time that included a commitment to restore a democratically elected council by October 2013. But Local Government Minister David Carter and Environment Minister Amy Adams backtracked on that when they announced in September 2012 that the commissioners would remain in place until 2016.

Past and present local-body politicians widely condemned the decision, claiming Cantabrians were being robbed of their voice in decision-making and accusing the government of using the earthquakes as an excuse for holding on to power. They argued there was no justification for cancelling elections and that Canterbury residents deserved a say in who represented them and made decisions on their behalf. Official papers showed even the commissioners did not think they should continue in office at the expense of regional council elections. Lawyers and human rights groups decried the decision as a disturbing breach of people's constitutional rights to vote and people even took to the streets to protest, but the government refused to budge.

Confidential documents obtained by *The Press* under the Official Information Act suggest one of the reasons the government is determined to keep the commissioners in place is that it wants to protect an agriculture boom potentially worth more than $5 billion to the national economy. But the government's detractors fear there is a more sinister plan in play — that at the heart of the government's decision to keep the commissioners is a desire to overhaul the structure of local government in Canterbury, to perhaps create another super-city, like Auckland. It is an interesting proposition, and one that many believe is worthy of investigation as it could save money and avoid the costly duplication of services.

ECan commissioners have told the government that now is not the right time for a single local government authority to run Canterbury but they believe it should be looked at in time for the 2016 local-body elections. Parker agrees. He reckons given the scale of change in the region, the shifts in residential population and the likelihood that the role and function of regional councils will become less complicated, it makes sense to look at how Canterbury governance could be rearranged.

'We do need to consider how we deliver local democracy in the most efficient and cost-effective way for our communities,' he says.

**THE OCTOBER 2013** local-body elections will bring more big changes to Christchurch's governance scene. A new-look council is likely to emerge after the elections, possibly with a different mayor at the helm. That will open the door for change, but some of the problems that have dogged the council in the post-quake era are likely to remain.

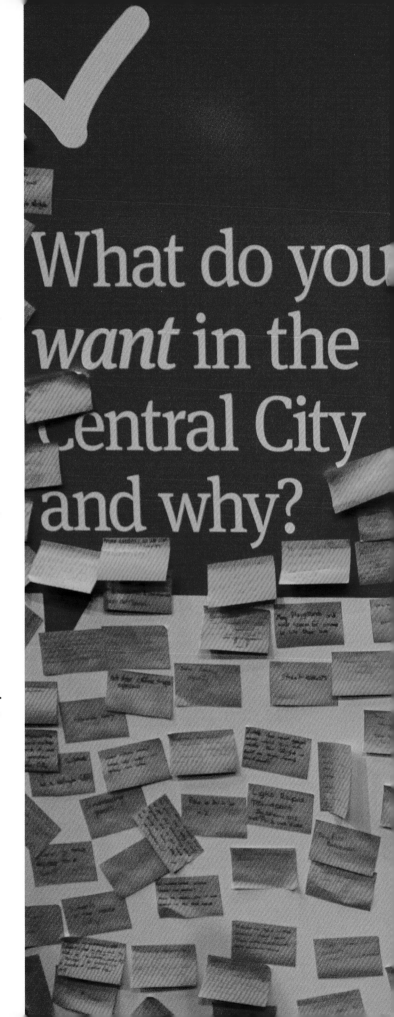

The tensions between the council and its more powerful next-door neighbour CERA will not disappear just because there are new faces around the council table; indeed, they could well increase. The new mayor and councillors may be more strident and less willing to play second fiddle to CERA. They may start exerting their authority more and push for a bigger say.

But the government is unlikely to tolerate the council pushing too far; it wants the rebuild to progress quickly and won't be pleased if the council stands in its way. It has already shown it is happy to sack locally elected representatives and replace them with commissioners if they are getting in the way, so it is unlikely Brownlee will put up with too much nonsense.

With a general election looming in 2014, though, the government will have to balance carefully its aspirations for a speedy rebuild and the community's growing resentment of autocratic decision-making. The community has lost its right to representation on one local authority; it is unlikely to tolerate losing another.

Thought will have to be given too to the long-term governance arrangements in Christchurch and Canterbury. CERA isn't going to be around forever — indeed, it is due to cease existing in 2016. What happens then? The rebuild will be in full swing but there will still be lots of work to be done. Who will provide the oversight? Who will step up and take control?

The ground may be shaking less in Christchurch now than it was two years ago but the turbulent times are far from over. ■

What do you *want* in the Central City and why?

Pennsylvania State University seismologist Professor Kevin Furlong was in Christchurch when the September 4, 2010 earthquake ripped apart a section of the Canterbury Plains. Here he studies the Greendale Fault scarp.
**DAVID HALLETT**

# SCIENCE
## A LAND RIPPED APART

*Paul Gorman*

The man with the black windjacket strides north along Liverpool St past the Audi on a lunchtime stroll on February 22, 2011. At the same time, just after 12.51pm, on the other side of the city, a group of visitors gather around the counter talking to a member of staff in the Christchurch Art Gallery shop.

**ABOUT NOW THE** previously unknown Port Hills Fault begins ripping apart across three segments, starting about 5 km down marginally to the west of the northern entrance to the Lyttelton road tunnel. In just a second or two the first, 'P', waves hit the city like a truck hitting the side of a building. The visitors in the art-gallery shop are pushed against the counter; shelves and stacks of books start to rock as the power goes off.

In Liverpool St, the man striding down the footpath and a younger man crossing the road react to the P wave. Stumbling out into the street as the Audi's alarm starts to go off, the older man struggles to stay upright as the violent 'S' waves arrive, peaking with a huge shake just six seconds after the first shudder.

That same vigorous movement in the gallery shop is evidenced by a massive shunt from south to north that sends stands flying and empties shelves. It is this unbelievably strong shaking force, which instruments later confirmed was unprecedented in New Zealand, that speeds up the demise of buildings that have in the past few seconds started crumbling across the city. The intense shaking lasts about 12 or 13 seconds and

**TOP LEFT** The side wall of Stonehurst Backpackers in Gloucester St collapsed due to the violent shaking of the magnitude 6.3, February 22, 2011 quake.
**RICHARD COSGROVE**

**BOTTOM** The Lyttelton clock, barely a kilometre or two from the quake's epicentre, was running four minutes fast when the shaking stopped it.
**NATASHA MARTIN**

the very worst of it only a few seconds. The quake dies away quickly after about 18 seconds.

With the benefit of hindsight — in this case courtesy of closed-circuit television and internet site YouTube — we can look back uneasily on these scenes with a ghoulish knowledge of what is about to happen.

In one sense that prescience gives us an almost God-like view of events. In another, it reminds us of times when something dramatic has happened in our lives and we think how blissfully unaware of it we were seconds, minutes, hours or days beforehand. 'It's best not to think about what's round the corner,' we tell ourselves comfortingly.

What did lie around the corner for Christchurch folk after the shock and tragedy of the February earthquake was, in terms of big quakes, pretty much more of the same. While the city's population tried to apply the philosophy of not worrying about things that were out of their control, of not wasting effort thinking about the inevitable aftershocks, realistically they were never far from the mind.

The powerful magnitude 7.1 earthquake on September 4, 2010 shattered not just the region's serenity but its stability too. Seven or eight hidden faults beneath the Canterbury Plains gravels were involved in the complex event, including the Greendale Fault, the longest structure, which ruptured from about 10 to 15 km down right through to the surface. The quake's total magnitude was a result of the seven to eight moderate to large quakes triggered on each of those faults.

The fault that broke five months later and generated the deadly February quake that changed Christchurch forever would have ruptured eventually.

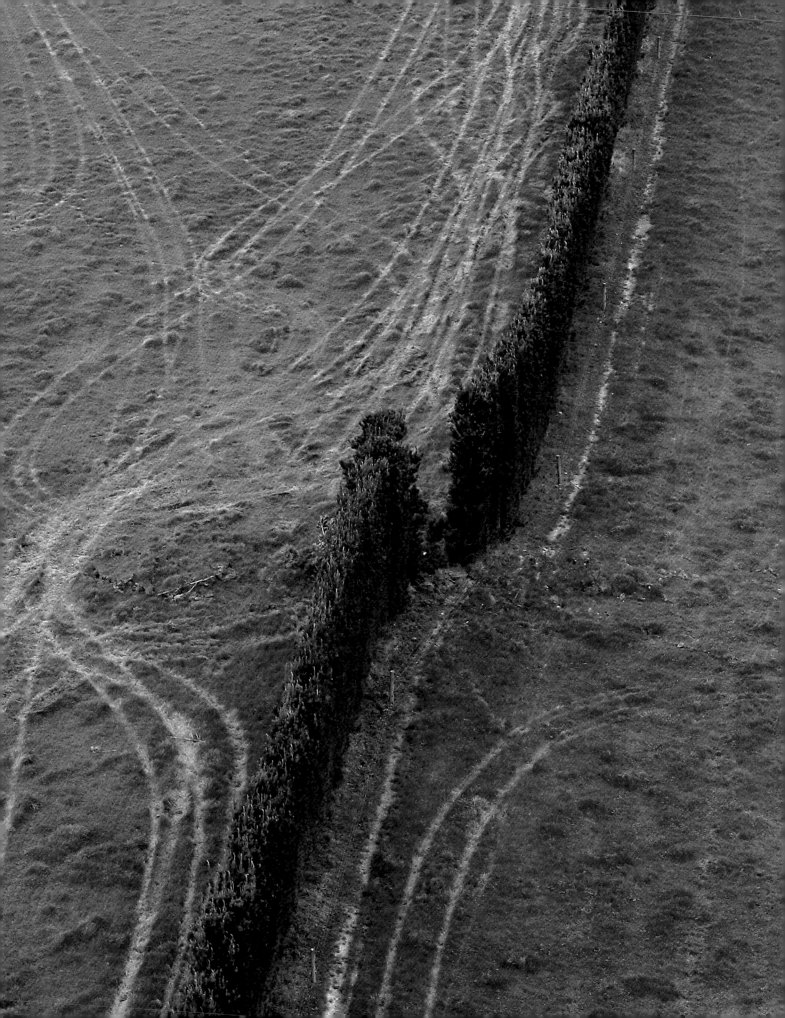

But is it possible that the readjustment of stresses in the basement rocks may have accelerated matters by a few dozen or hundred years?

Similarly, just as things under the city seemed to be quietening down again through the autumn of 2011 and into the winter, the ground showed it had other ideas. On June 13, a crystal-clear frosty day in Christchurch, the earth heaved in dramatic fashion. A minute after one o'clock that afternoon, segments of two more hitherto unknown faults ripped apart significantly, this time close to Clifton and Sumner, generating a magnitude 5.9 quake. Just an hour and 19 minutes later, a much larger tear on the same fault patch but a little further west generated a long-lasting and damaging magnitude 6.4 quake. This was felt across the South Island and as far north as New Plymouth, and caused extensive damage and further rockfalls from Sumner to Clifton around to Redcliffs.

The almost immediate psychological effect of these quakes on the people of Christchurch cannot be underestimated. Residents had become used to living with frequent, sometimes large, aftershocks and were also familiar with the pattern of experiencing increasingly small tremors after a bigger shake. They thought they had it worked out. On this occasion, though, for the first time, there was a clear foreshock followed by a main shock. Such a

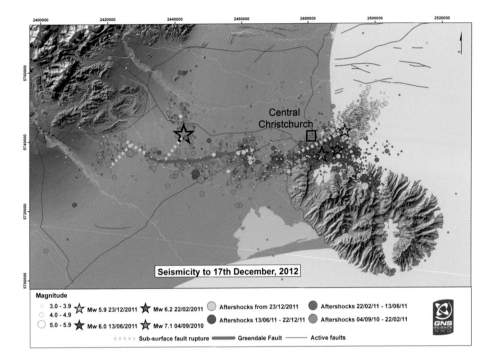

Magnitude

| | |
|---|---|
| · 3.0 - 3.9 | ☆ Mw 5.9 23/12/2011 ★ Mw 6.2 22/02/2011 ⚪ Aftershocks from 23/12/2011 ⚫ Aftershocks 22/02/11 - 13/06/11 |
| ○ 4.0 - 4.9 | ⚫ Aftershocks 13/06/11 - 22/12/11 ⚫ Aftershocks 04/09/10 - 22/02/11 |
| ○ 5.0 - 5.9 | ★ Mw 6.0 13/06/2011 ★ Mw 7.1 04/09/2010 |

····· Sub-surface fault rupture ▬▬ Greendale Fault ── Active faults

Seismicity to 17th December, 2012

sudden change in the 'rules' unnerved many. It was not to be the only time.

The difficulty for residents and scientists alike, of course, is that until you get the second, bigger, quake, it is impossible to know the first one was a warning shot. Afterwards, GNS Science said the only real benefit in terms of preparedness was that the foreshock got some people out of buildings or situations where they might have been more exposed to danger in the second quake.

Later scientific analysis found the two faults responsible lay almost at right angles to each other. One had a similar east-north-east/west-south-west orientation to the Port Hills and Greendale faults. But the other was perpendicular to that, on a north-north-west/south-south-east line, running roughly parallel with and just offshore from Brighton Spit, close to Sumner and across through Godley Head toward Port Levy. While that orientation seemed to be at odds with that of most other Canterbury Plains faults, scientists said it conformed with the theory in which lines of stress lie at an angle across the predominating fault direction.

By the end of June the largest of the aftershocks from what became known as the 'double whammy' had died away and from July 2011 through to almost Christmas that year Christchurch enjoyed a period of relative seismic calm. But on December 23, as the city made final preparations for the big day two days hence, it happened again. Incredibly, it was just as hundreds of workplaces were being locked up for the summer and thousands of employees were sitting down for an end-of-year beer or wine

**LEFT** Four distinct earthquake aftershock sequences are visible in this GNS Science map of seismic events in central Canterbury between September 4, 2010 and December 17, 2012. 'The Gap', an area of subdued activity around Prebbleton and Lincoln, can be seen between the eastern end of the Greendale Fault and the western tip of the subsurface Port Hills Fault.

**TOP** More rockfalls occurred near Sumner on December 23, 2011, as magnitude 5.8 and 6.0 quakes struck within an hour and 20 minutes of each other.
**IAIN MCGREGOR**

**MIDDLE TOP** Christchurch's eastern suburbs, including Broadhaven Ave in Parklands, were badly affected by liquefaction again in the December 23, 2011 quakes.
**IAIN MCGREGOR**

**MIDDLE BOTTOM** A bus carefully weaves its way over badly damaged roads and water and sand from liquefaction on New Brighton Rd near the Pages Rd bridge on December 23.
**DEAN KOZANIC**

**BOTTOM** A large sinkhole caused by liquefaction opened up underneath this ute.
**IAIN MCGREGOR**

and barbecue lunch in the sun. Heralded by a thunderous, heart-stopping rumble, regarded by many as the loudest to accompany any quake since the September 4 main shock, a magnitude 5.8 quake rippled across the city, generating more liquefaction, loosening more rocks on the Port Hills and causing further damage.

Uncannily, it turned out to be another double-whammy event. Even more unnervingly, the interval between the foreshock and the magnitude 6.0 main shock was almost the same as in June, perhaps a minute longer at an hour and 20 minutes. This time, though, there were 5.2 and 5.5 magnitude shakes between the two. It was an extremely cruel blow for residents who were starting to put the year's awful events behind them, and particularly so for those who dared and hoped to believe the earth under their city might finally be relenting.

The quakes were located between 2 and 5 km offshore from Brighton Spit on what later analysis showed was probably the eastern, seaward, extension of the same 'central city' fault responsible for the Boxing Day 2010 magnitude 4.9 quake. Seismic surveying in 2011 by scientists from the University of Canterbury and the University of Calgary had uncovered this feature, running from Riccarton underneath the city centre and across the eastern suburbs to New Brighton beach.

After Christmas that year the ground below the city started to settle down, though there was a resurgence of strong aftershocks on the night of New Year's Day 2012, and occasional quakes during the week after. The gradual decline in aftershock magnitude and frequency continued throughout the year, with only four shakes of magnitude 5 or higher, three of them in the first half of January and the last on May 25. By year's end there was only the occasional, perhaps monthly, tremor of magnitude 4 or just over.

Such quiescence was cautiously welcomed by the Canterbury community. But never far from people's minds, given their previous experience of major events after more settled periods, was the realisation that things could ramp up at any time. Some had even become superstitious about quakes, fearing that talking or even thinking about them being largely over was likely to spark them off again. Putting aside such fears, though, logic was suggesting that central Canterbury was, by and large, through the worst of the quake sequence and into the long tail of the quake probability decay curve. However, tempering such optimism was the recognition that there could still be other unknown, hidden faults below the aftershock zone — as well as those around the region already catalogued — that were more than capable of generating magnitude 6 or higher earthquakes.

In May 2011, after an outcry from the public and media about being kept in the dark over quake forecasts that were being calculated by GNS Science, the Crown Research Institute began releasing the aftershock probabilities it had been providing to the Canterbury Earthquake Recovery Authority (CERA). Christchurch city councillor Sue Wells was the catalyst for change. She and other councillors and community board members had been told of the risk of another large quake at a CERA meeting chaired by Canterbury Earthquake Recovery Minister Gerry Brownlee. Wells then put the figures on her website at a time when anxious Cantabrians were still waiting to find out what scientists had found below the city and the Canterbury Plains using geophysical imaging, including ground-penetrating radar.

Those May 2011 figures, released just two weeks before the June 13 event, put the chance of a quake, before June 2012, of between magnitude 6.0 and 7.0 at 23 per cent. There was also a more than 90 per cent chance of a magnitude 5.0 to 6.0 shake in the next 12 months, falling to more than a 70 per cent chance in the following year. The figures were not just for Christchurch but for the whole aftershock zone, from Sheffield in the west to Rangiora in the north, Lincoln in the south and across Banks Peninsula.

GNS Science continued to update the aftershock forecasts with their slowly dropping probabilities throughout 2011 and 2012. By the end of 2012 the probability of a magnitude 5.0 to 5.4 shake in the 12 months to December 2013 was 69 per cent, down from 82 per cent in January 2012. Across the same period the institute forecast there was a 29 per cent chance of a magnitude 5.5 to 5.9 quake in the zone, a 9 per cent probability of a magnitude 6.0 to 6.4 aftershock, and a 2 per cent risk of a magnitude 6.5 to 6.9 event. The probability of a magnitude 7 or higher quake in the next year remained unchanged at 1 per cent, due to the closeness of other large faults in the Canterbury foothills and high country.

**MORE THAN TWO** and a half years on from the first major quake, central Canterbury remained a happy hunting ground for seismologists, geologists, geomorphologists and geophysicists from around the country and overseas. Several dozen research papers had already been published on the earthquake sequence and more work was under way. Japanese researchers were investigating the June 13, 2011 quakes while a team of five scientists from GNS Science was looking in more detail at the events of December 23, 2011.

One of the interesting features of the Canterbury earthquake sequence is that several different timescales are at play. After a quake, the public and the media demand information almost instantly. Yet good science takes time to research, analyse and publish — certainly months and sometimes even years. Throughout the Canterbury quakes, scientists have often found themselves caught in the media spotlight and having to respond rapidly to the clamouring for details. As is to be expected, some have been better at dealing with the public than others.

*Geological time, of course, is the grand backdrop against which all this has happened. It is incomprehensibly vast, a gargantuan canvas on which our activities and lifespans amount to barely a speck of dirt on a grain of dust.*

Geological time, of course, is the grand backdrop against which all this has happened. It is incomprehensibly vast, a gargantuan canvas on which our activities and lifespans amount to barely a speck of dirt on a grain of dust. To Canterbury folk, the quakes seem to have been a part of their existence for a long time, but two and a half years is not even the blink of an eye on this mammoth timescale. Scientists estimate that the faults that have ruptured around the region only do so every 10,000 or so years, but even that interval pales into insignificance compared with the hundreds of millions and billions of years that some geological features elsewhere have been in existence.

Work in 2012 by Canterbury University and GNS Science in central Canterbury helped confirm approximately how many years there are between major events on the Greendale Fault. Soon after the September 4, 2010 quake ripped a gash across the Plains, landowners, utility companies and roading authorities began ploughing, rewiring and straightening work that largely removed evidence of the fault's dislocation on the landscape. Apart from a few piles of gravel by the side of the road, the odd bump on the road surface and some strange kinks in shelter belts, there is now little left physically that shows the violence of that quake.

But signs of the fault's strength lie not far from the surface. Highfield Rd was literally cut in two by the fault. In a field behind a line of trees on the eastern side of the road, PhD student Sharon Hornblow and her supervisor

Mark Quigley arranged the excavation of a 30-metre-long, 4-metre-deep trench across the fault to allow them to research past movements and collect organic material for radiocarbon dating. They found that features at the surface and in an old stream channel about a metre down in the trench had been displaced about 65 cm horizontally and 10 cm vertically by the fault. But a much older stream channel near the bottom of the trench had been offset horizontally by about 120 cm and vertically by 20 cm, double the amounts closer to the surface.

From that they inferred that large quakes from the Greendale Fault had shifted the land twice in the roughly 16,000 years the deeper gravels had lain there. As the size of each shunt was about the same, it also meant the magnitude of the quakes was similar. Further work is now being done on the organic material found in the trench to more accurately date the large quake that occurred prior to 2010.

According to Mark Quigley, the amount of movement of objects deeper in the trench compared with those on the surface showed the 2010 quake was the first to rupture the ground surface for more than about 5000 years. 'The easiest explanation is that a major, surface-rupturing earthquake occurred at this location some time after the deposition of the older [deeper] sand channels but prior to deposition of the younger [shallower] sand channels.'

Other data gathered using ground-penetrating radar showed sediments toward the bottom of the trench were tilted more than the shallower layers.

Quigley believes that could either be a result of the river environment in which the sediments were deposited or that they had been folded by past quakes.

A big question that has intrigued scientists and bothered the public is the relationship between the eastern end of the Greendale Fault and the western tip of the Port Hills Fault. In the eyes of many it seems logical that the two are related somehow and that strands of both faults might come close to linking up with one another. Some even believe the two faults might actually just be one fault. Scientists have generally discounted that theory, pointing out that the mystery zone around Prebbleton and Lincoln known widely as 'The Gap' separates the ends of the two faults.

However, bucking that trend, in 2012 University of Southern California seismologist Yong-Gang Li and Canterbury University scientists Greg De Pascale, Darren Gravely and Mark Quigley discovered the faults were 'moderately' connected several kilometres underground. A consequence of that finding is that Christchurch probably had a narrow escape from a much larger earthquake, possibly of as much as magnitude 7.4, in September 2010.

Li, the lead researcher, said that if, on that day, the two faults had ruptured together along their combined length of about 70 km — from the Plains under the city to the sea — they could have produced a quake about twice as strong as the magnitude 7.1 event, which luckily had been centred

much further away from the city near Darfield. Fortunately, stronger rock structures in the 'step-over zone' (where the fault breaks up into small segments roughly parallel but offset from each other, like steps) at the eastern end of the Greendale Fault near The Gap actually stopped the rupture in its tracks.

The researchers deployed two sets of seismic equipment after the February 22, 2011 earthquake — one array across the central part of the Greendale Fault where it had broken through to the surface and the other at Princess Margaret Hospital in Cashmere above the blind Port Hills Fault (the Port Hills Fault was 'blind', like lots of the faults under the Canterbury Plains, in that it did not rupture up to the surface, so we cannot see it). Between May and September 2011, the seismometers recorded more than 1000 aftershocks of magnitude 1.0 to 6.0.

Li's group analysed the data and identified that waves of energy from the quakes on both faults were trapped inside the fault zones and travelling along them. The Greendale Fault apparatus recorded its own aftershocks but also those from the Port Hills Fault.

'It was a surprise,' Li said. 'Our interpretation is that between the two faults there is a connection at depth — seismic depth somewhere below 3 km — showing the faults are moderately connected.'

From the trapped waves the researchers calculated the Greendale Fault extended eastwards underground by another 5 to 8 km. The main rupture of the Port Hills Fault also appeared to run further west toward the other fault. Mark Quigley noted that the strong rock structures at the eastern tip of the Greendale Fault were complicated and had acted as a rupture barrier.

'There appear to be some buried thrusts near the eastern end of the Greendale system that would have helped to accommodate much of the displacement during the Darfield earthquake. Given the significant stress drop in the Darfield quake, it would seem that, if this was a crossable barrier, then it could have been breached [if the faults were linked].'

Another discussion point for many has been how and why the September 4 earthquake sparked so many other major quakes and thousands of aftershocks. It had generally been accepted that the February 22 event was triggered by the September quake and was a late and large aftershock. The unspoken implication of that was to suggest the Port Hills Fault — once it was known about — was not a structure with its own history and foibles, primed and ready to go at any time regardless of what had happened a bit over five months earlier.

GNS Science researchers doing after-the-event background checks on the Port Hills Fault discovered the February quake could actually have happened at any time over the next few decades or centuries. The fault had

Research by GNS Science seismologist Bill Fry and others showed the fault that generated the February 22, 2011 quake was already highly stressed and might not have needed the September quake as a trigger.

**PHOTO SUPPLIED**

not needed the readjustment in crustal stresses following the September event to set it off.

The team of 10, including seismologist Bill Fry, compared the amount of energy released in each event, the stress of the ground and how the volcanic massif of Banks Peninsula affected the shaking. They used Coulomb failure stress (CFS), a measure of a fault's state and how close it might be to breaking, to show changes in regional ground stresses after the September quake.

Fry said faults across central Canterbury had been greatly stressed before the first quake. Researchers then found that stress on the Port Hills Fault increased after the September quake by what they described as only a 'modest' amount — less than 0.1 of a megapascal. 'This amount is much smaller than CFS changes elsewhere in the region, suggesting that the fault that failed in the February event was already highly stressed and close to failure prior to September.'

Those conclusions raise the spectre that if the February quake had been the first in the sequence Christchurch would have been hit even harder. Quigley believes it was fortunate that many at-risk buildings had been damaged and earmarked for demolition after the September earthquake. 'It's easy to forget how much damage had been caused to buildings in Christchurch and around the region by the September quake. A lot of us felt like we got off lightly after that quake, because of the time of day. If that had happened at a different time of day there would have been fatalities.

'Some of those areas were still cordoned off in February, some of those buildings had already come down. Who's to say they wouldn't all have come right down in the February quake? The February quake could have actually had a worse death toll if that September quake had not happened.'

The research by Fry and others also showed Banks Peninsula acted like a reflector in September, with reflecting waves interfering with arriving waves and increasing the size of earth movements. However, they say that in February it appeared the peninsula acted more like an oscillator, briefly absorbing wave energy from the Port Hills Fault's rupture and gradually releasing it, extending the duration of shaking.

Amazingly, high-precision satellite readings and global positioning system (GPS) measurements show Canterbury is still moving and settling as it accommodates stress changes from the lengthy quake sequence. Data shows the land beneath Christchurch and the eastern Plains is continuing to deform by several millimetres a year.

Work by GNS Science geophysicists, led by the late John Beavan, revealed what is known as post-seismic deformation, which they considered could be due to slow fault-slip around the edges of the faults that broke in the larger quakes. Deformation around the city was especially marked in the months after the February event, while displacement at a rate of up to 10 mm a year in response to the June 13 quakes continued through 2012.

In September 2012, Beavan said the researchers had actually been surprised by the small amounts of deformation, which he put down to the strength of the rock layers that ruptured under the Plains. The extreme ground accelerations experienced in the quakes are also believed to be due to that crustal strength.

'It's changing less than we expected. The more well-developed faults often have a mix of brittle and less-brittle patches. The brittle parts break in a quake and put more stress on the more ductile patches.

'Those increased stresses cause those patches to slip and this slip can take place over weeks or months. That can account for 20 to 30 per cent of the movements seen in the earthquake itself. But in this case it's small, just a few per cent, and we think that's because the crust is so strong in this area.'

The research team also found that short- to medium-term surface deformation could be caused by changes to underground water bodies in the aftermath of a quake. Surface changes over a longer period were also possible as a result of the movement of more flexible rocks deeper down in the crust where the temperature was higher.

Despite all the shaking from the quakes and the region's continuing deformation, a team of United States scientists said in mid-2012 that the direction of the stress field across Canterbury had not changed. That made future large quakes on

other unknown faults less likely, they concluded comfortingly. Pennsylvania State University seismologist Kevin Furlong, who was a visiting professor at Canterbury University during the early days of the quake sequence, viewed the finding as an 'interesting' one.

At any particular time, Canterbury is effectively being squeezed by the anticlockwise movement of the Pacific Plate, which is pushing into the Australian Plate. The resistance from the Alpine Fault — the boundary of the Pacific and Australian plates — and the Hope Fault and Marlborough fault systems against this squeezing is pushing back across Canterbury in an east-south-east direction, determining the direction of more local faulting.

Furlong said nearly all the faults that had produced quakes in the aftershock zone since September 2010 were oriented within about 40 compass degrees of the broad east-south-east-pointing stress field. Faults pointing in a different direction were less likely to be able to rupture unless that stress field changed. 'We looked at about 150 of the main events and aftershocks and virtually all provided the same orientation for the stress. If there were to be other activity, we would expect it to have similar orientations to this sequence.

'The interesting results from this work were the stress field did not change at all throughout the entire sequence, which means it is unlikely to change now. If it had changed, you might expect we wouldn't be able to discount the fact that other faults in a different orientation might also become active.'

Each large quake was similar to the others and had been reasonably self-contained. The February event had 'defined a very specific footprint' but did not reactivate the main part of the September rupture. The June quakes exhibited the same characteristics, not kicking off in any major way the February or September faults.

**THE EXTENDED AND** unusual Canterbury earthquake sequence has given scientists from around the world plenty of material for their studies. Their work has also been informed by some of the best quake data ever gathered, thanks to the foresight and determination over many years of local engineers and scientists to put in place a comprehensive network of ground-motion sensing equipment.

The researchers' findings have been interesting in themselves but have also given some comfort to Cantabrians who have had to cope with thousands of quakes. It always helps to have some explanation for what is going on.

Many aspects of the sequence are still unknown, of course, but the mysteries of The Gap remain a significant concern. This is believed to be the last area around Christchurch that has faults with the potential to generate a significant earthquake. Some scientists have warned that careful monitoring of The Gap is essential and should be a priority for government research funding.

The Gap is a physical void — the area between the eastern tip of the Greendale Fault and the western end of the Port Hills Fault — but also a zone where scientists have calculated there is a numerical 'gap' in the amount of energy released by quakes compared with that liberated close to the two big faults on either side. Despite that, the area has already generated three very sharply felt quakes of magnitude 5.0 or higher — in October 2010 and in January and June 2011 — and more than 30 aftershocks of between 4.0 and 5.0, some of these in swarms in short succession that alarmed local residents.

Canterbury University and GNS Science researchers have spent time studying The Gap and recommend it as a funding priority. Underground surveying of the zone has found fault structures that appear to reach within several hundred metres of the surface in places. However, Quigley believes it is unlikely any of the fault segments are long enough to generate a quake of above magnitude 6.

Beavan's GNS Science geophysics team also looked at The Gap in 2012 and questioned why it had not released as much seismic energy as might be expected. Two months before he died in November 2012, Beavan said the research group was trying to get funding from the government's natural hazards platform to continue monitoring. 'There are possible reasons why this region will not fail in an earthquake or earthquakes during the present sequence,' he said. 'For example, faults in this region may have failed relatively recently compared to the faults that have broken in the present sequence, so even the increases in stress due to the recent earthquakes are insufficient to cause failure.

'But the truth is that we do not know whether or not this region is likely to fail in the near future, nor, if it did, whether it would be as a single earthquake or as several smaller earthquakes. We think it is of high importance to continue and expand ongoing monitoring of this region, in case this will provide clues to its future behaviour.'

The researchers carried out an approximately four-monthly GPS survey of 30 points from February 2012 but said it would be at least a year before any conclusions could be drawn.

Kevin Furlong commented that important lessons had been learned since the region woke up to the vigorous shaking on September 4, 2010. 'Perhaps one of the biggest lessons we have learned has come from the recognition that in any major earthquake system it is not just the initial

**TOP** Tonnes of sand and silt from liquefaction in the December 23, 2011 quakes choked roads in the city's east, including Queenspark Dr in Parklands.
**DEAN KOZANIC**

**BOTTOM** Here we go again. Grandad Jim Niven takes a break the day after the December quakes from digging out the Rawson St, New Brighton, house where he lives with his son Peter.
**DEAN KOZANIC**

Children play on a pile of sand from liquefaction in Parklands as a road cone decorated before the December quakes gives a seasonal message.
**DEAN KOZANIC**

event that matters. Particularly in places like Canterbury, where we don't have a good record of how an earthquake sequence will play out, it is important not to too quickly assume it will behave like some other well-defined fault system.

'Plate-boundary fault systems like the San Andreas in California or the Alpine Fault in New Zealand are better understood than what we term intra-plate fault systems, and the Canterbury faults seem to behave more like intra-plate faults.

'The second big lesson is certainly the liquefaction story. Liquefaction has long been recognised as one of the most damaging aspects of earthquakes to buildings and infrastructure. The 1964 Alaska and the 1985 Mexico City quakes had substantial damage associated with liquefaction, but they were both "great" earthquakes, larger than magnitude 8, and so the extensive liquefaction throughout Canterbury after the September earthquake was certainly an important lesson.

'This message was reinforced when liquefaction recurred repeatedly with each moderate aftershock. I think most of us would not have thought that magnitude 5 earthquakes could generate significant liquefaction, yet in the liquefaction-prone areas such was the case.'

The gradual absorption, over thousands of years, of gigantic forces from the inexorable turning and colliding of crustal plates ultimately led to the sudden, catastrophic failure of the blind faults beneath the Canterbury Plains. It was just our collective bad luck that it happened in our lifetime, Furlong said.

'Along plate boundaries, such as the Alpine Fault, the earthquakes and the stresses that cause them tend to change in character after the main events occur, because the stress regime changes substantially during the main earthquakes. In the Canterbury case it seems rather that, although the overall stress level has almost certainly been reduced, the cause of the earthquakes was not the accumulating of slip deficit along the Greendale Fault, as would be the case along the Alpine Fault, but rather that the whole region was being stressed.

'That was likely as a result of the collision between the Pacific and Australia plates across New Zealand. The Greendale Fault was simply the weak link that cracked and started the sequence.' ∎

Appointed members of the
Canterbury Earthquakes Royal
Commission Richard Fenwick,
left, Sir Ron Carter and
chairman Justice Mark Cooper,
meet in a rented Merivale
house in June 2011, four
months before the hearings
began at a church hall in
Riccarton.
**DEAN KOZANIC**

# THE ROYAL COMMISSION

## WHAT WENT WRONG, AND HOW CAN WE DO BETTER?

*Marc Greenhill*

What went wrong? It was the question asked by many
Cantabrians in the aftermath of the February 22 earthquake.
Three men were charged with uncovering the answers, and
their conclusions would be scrutinised by the world.

**THE CANTERBURY EARTHQUAKES** Royal Commission was formed in April 2011, with Auckland High Court judge Justice Mark Cooper at the helm. Justice Cooper was joined by Sir Ron Carter, a former president of the Association of Consulting Engineers New Zealand who holds an honorary engineering doctorate, and Richard Fenwick, an adjunct associate professor in civil engineering at the University of Canterbury. The Commission determined that the inquiry would include any building within the central business district that failed causing loss of life.

The largest loss was in the Canterbury Television (CTV) building in Madras St, where 115 people died. A further 18 died in the Pyne Gould Corporation (PGC) building in Cambridge Tce, and another 36 people were killed in other parts of the CBD. In addition to the CTV and PGC buildings, the *Press* building in Cathedral Square, the Link Centre in High St, the Methodist Church on Durham St as well as numerous commercial premises on Colombo St, Cashel St, Gloucester St, Hereford St, Lichfield St and Manchester St were investigated. The Commission also widened the inquiry to include any other building in the suburbs that caused loss of life, which included commercial premises on Riccarton Rd, Coleridge St in Sydenham, Worcester St in Linwood and a residential property in St Albans.

Justice Cooper was quoted as saying the February disaster was 'one of the most closely observed earthquakes ever'. The Commission's findings would be scrutinised by international quake and building design experts, and media, from countries that had lost citizens. Any recommendations would not be legally binding, as it was up to the government to decide law changes, nor would the Commission deal with who was liable for injury or death. Justice Cooper said that even if the commissioners found that buildings had not complied with standards, their

findings would not apportion blame.

Two independent lawyers — Stephen Mills QC and Christchurch Crown prosecutor Mark Zarifeh — were appointed to act as counsel for the Commission.

Christchurch lawyer Marcus Elliott was also appointed to act for the victims' families, despite the government having initially ruled out a third counsel. Prime Minister John Key had come under pressure since he had given personal assurances soon after the quake that the government would help families 'as best we can'.

'In the final analysis, the families felt a little vulnerable and they have a high degree of anxiety. We obviously have great sympathy for their position,' Key said at the time.

The hearings themselves began with a simple opening ceremony on October 17, 2011. It took 10 minutes and 49 seconds for the victims' names to be read out. Each name was followed by a pause, honouring every individual life lost. Hands were held in support and tears were shed as about a hundred people gathered outside Riccarton's St Teresa's church hall. The Reverend Maurice Gray of Ngai Tahu welcomed grieving family members and the public with a moving prayer in Maori, and pupils from the kapa haka group at St Teresa's School sang an Irish blessing to family members.

Over the next 11 months, hearings were held on seismicity, soils, unreinforced masonry buildings, the PGC building, the Forsyth Barr and

The Royal Commission, sitting in the St Teresa's Church hall in Riccarton, hears from Kestrel Group director David Brunsdon, extreme left, about New Zealand's building safety evaluation process.

**STACY SQUIRES**

Hotel Grand Chancellor buildings, other buildings that caused loss of life, new building technologies, the training and organisation of engineers, building assessments after earthquakes, building codes and design rules, and the ill-fated CTV building.

**ALTHOUGH THE COMMISSION** had stressed the inquiry was not about apportioning blame, the failure of the CTV building came under intense scrutiny during an eight-week hearing. More than 80 witnesses gave evidence about the initial building consent issued by the Christchurch City Council, the construction and design of the building, the identification of a structural weakness in 1990, and the assessments after the September 4 and Boxing Day quakes in 2010.

CTV receptionist Maryanne Jackson was one of the first survivors to be heard when the hearing opened on June 25, 2012. Jackson, the only CTV employee in the building to survive its collapse and subsequent fire, told the Commission she felt unsafe in the building and often ran outside during large aftershocks after the September 2010 quake. This habit saved her life when the quake struck at 12.51pm on February 22. She fled across Madras St soon after the shaking started.

The sound was 'horrific, like a jet plane landing on the roof', Jackson said. 'About three-quarters of the way across the road I looked over my shoulder slightly. I could see the [building] collapsing behind me. It felt like the building was chasing me as I ran.

'I would have been across the road in seconds. When I turned around, the building was completely down. It had pancaked, with all six levels down to just rubble.'

Further terrifying witness accounts were given in the hearing's opening days. Key players emerged, some of whom shifted blame or failed to recall major details. Others showed contrition or apologised for the roles they had played.

Alan Reay, principal of the firm that designed the CTV building, distanced himself from the project personally but said his firm was 'ultimately responsible' if design flaws were shown to be the reason for the collapse. Reay said during the hearing that he had worked for only three hours on the project, and it was difficult to know what might have been if he had led the design. A Building and Housing Department report released in February 2012 identified serious design and construction flaws in the building and found it did not meet building standards. Reay dismissed the report as 'technically inadequate'.

Employees described Reay as being difficult to work for, and evidence was given that it was common for him to go over the heads of Christchurch City Council engineers if they questioned his designs. Reay later issued an apology, saying the building did not meet his standards.

David Harding, the engineer who led the design project for Reay's company, had little experience in designing multi-storey buildings or in using the computer modelling programme Etabs, with which he had tested the seismic strength of the CTV design. Harding said he relied on his employer for 'guidance', but Reay said Harding was 'competent to undertake the work' and should have raised concerns about his experience.

Harding believed the CTV building collapsed because it faced unexpectedly high vertical forces in the quake that it was never designed, or required to be designed, to withstand. He admitted that spiral-steel reinforcing in the building's column joints was too widely spaced and concrete columns had not been designed to absorb the force of an earthquake, but said this had no effect on its fate. He, too, later apologised to the victims' families, saying the collapse was an engineer's 'worst-nightmare scenario'.

The commissioners found that Reay should have supervised Harding's work, given his lack of multi-storey experience. 'We do not accept that it was appropriate for Dr Reay to rely on Mr Harding's confidence that he could do the design and then leave him to it without putting any checks in place,' the final report said.

They found Harding was 'acting outside his competence' on the CTV building, based on 'fundamental deficiencies' of the design. 'Mr Harding erred in his self-assessment of his competence and the confidence he had that he could design this building competently was unfounded.'

Gerald Shirtcliff, the CTV site's construction manager, initially refused to appear at the hearing and was later exposed as having faked his engineering qualifications. The commissioners had 'serious issues' with his credibility and found that he was not 'up to the job'. 'We conclude that Mr Shirtcliff simply did not spend sufficient time on site in order to adequately perform the role of a construction manager.'

John Drew, the CTV building manager and owner of fourth-level tenant The Clinic, spent more than four hours giving evidence. He came under fire for having the building checked by structural engineer David Coatsworth only once after the September 2010 quake and not supplying the building plans. The file would have revealed a 1990 report stating there was a 'vital area of non-compliance'. Drew said he believed the building was safe because the council issued green stickers after the September and Boxing Day quakes in 2010. He offered his condolences to the victims' families at the hearing, saying he felt a 'huge sense of responsibility'.

The Christchurch City Council decision to issue the building's consent

**TOP** During the hearings into the collapse of the CTV building, David Harding, a structural engineer for Alan Reay Consulting at the time, gave evidence about the building-permit process.
**DEAN KOZANIC**

**BOTTOM** CTV building manager John Drew spent more than four hours giving evidence and said he felt a 'huge sense of responsibility' for believing the building was safe after the city council green-stickered it following the September and Boxing Day 2010 quakes.
**STACY SQUIRES**

in 1986, and its rapid assessment procedures after the September and Boxing Day quakes in 2010, also came in for close scrutiny. Structural engineer Arthur O'Leary said the CTV building's 'pioneering' design meant the council's reviewing engineers would not have had the expertise to pick up faults nor would they have had the benefit of peer review.

The widow of council consents officer Graeme Tapper, who signed off the building in 1986, told the Commission her husband did not want to sign it off but was under 'huge pressure' from his boss, Bryan Bluck, and was concerned about his job. After the September 2010 quake, three council officers carried out a level two assessment without an engineer and issued a green sticker.

The Commission's final report, released in December 2012, found the building should not have been granted building consent in 1986. The commissioners found there were a number of non-complying aspects of the design because Harding was working 'beyond his competence', and that Reay did not review the design. This led to a building design that was 'deficient in a number of important respects', the report said.

Consent for construction was lodged in July 1986. The report noted council consenting officer Graeme Tapper's misgivings about the structural integrity of the design, and the fact that there is no record of his concerns being addressed. While questions were later raised about the expertise of council staff in assessing the building's 'pioneering' design, the commissioners found it was likely Reay convinced council chief engineer Bryan Bluck that concerns about the design were unfounded. The permit should not have been issued because the design did not comply with building bylaws, the report said.

Construction flaws, failure to act after problems were highlighted in a 1990 inspection, and post-quake checks were other areas of

concern. Williams Construction, led by managing director Michael Brooks, construction manager Gerald Shirtcliff and foreman Bill Jones, began building work in October 1986. The commissioners found that Jones was competent but lacked supervision, and that Shirtcliff did not spend sufficient time on-site to perform his role adequately.

A number of construction defects were identified after the collapse, including the absence of roughening of joints, and reinforcing bars within some precast beams not conforming to design. The report said the lack of roughening should have been visible to the engineer if he was carrying out regular site inspections, as well as to the foreman and construction manager.

In January 1990, Holmes Consulting Group prepared a structural report for a potential purchaser, the Canterbury Regional Council, which noted a 'vital area of non-compliance' in the tying of the floors to some of the shear walls and the fact that the building could separate from the shear core in an earthquake. Holmes recommended remedial work, including steel drag bars on all levels above the ground floor. The drag bars were installed in November 1991, but only on levels four, five and six, and no permit was sought. The commissioners found the identification of such a fundamental design error should have signalled the need for a more detailed review of the design.

The building was green-stickered after the September 2010 quake

Alan Reay, the principal of the company that designed the CTV building, said he had only worked on the project for three hours and called a Building and Housing Department report in February 2012 'technically inadequate' when it identified serious design and construction flaws in the building. Reay later apologised for the building not meeting his own standards.

**STACY SQUIRES**

following two rapid assessments by council inspectors. Building manager John Drew also employed structural engineer David Coatsworth, who completed a damage-based assessment and deemed the building safe to occupy. Coatsworth asked for structural drawings to be supplied, but did not receive them before finalising his report in October. His recommendations for further assessment were not carried out. A rapid assessment was completed after the Boxing Day quake, but no further detailed assessment was obtained. The commissioners found it would have been preferable for Coatsworth to have clearly explained the 'nature, extent and limitations' of his assessment.

Prime Minister John Key labelled the final CTV report 'grim and sobering reading', while Attorney-General Christopher Finlayson said it would have implications for the entire country.

Christchurch mayor Bob Parker apologised to the victims' families. 'It is clear, based on the evidence we have seen, there were shortcomings in those processes, but they were also one part of a very complex process that involved a number of other parties,' he said.

'Naturally, everybody [at the council] is truly sorry. Albeit it's in a historic context, but it doesn't lessen the pain for us at this time.'

**THE PYNE GOULD** Corporation building was doomed to fail.

The Commission's findings on the PGC building failure, which claimed 18 lives in the February 2011 earthquake, showed the structure had little chance of surviving the shake. Built in 1966, the five-storey structure needed much lower seismic strength than today to comply with building standards. It lacked the 'ductility' that allows modern buildings to bend and absorb force in a quake.

The building stood around a shear core — its strongest part — that ran in a north–south line, meaning it was stronger if shaken in that direction than east–west. Fortunately for the majority of those inside at the time, the collapse sequence helped minimise the casualties.

At the two-week hearing in December 2011, survivor David Sandeman described dropping 12 metres into a dark hole. 'It was too dark to see any details. You couldn't tell the time on your wristwatch . . . There was a glimmer of light in the distance, I guess from where the floors had just pancaked together.'

Sandeman and four others were left trapped for more than two hours in a small enclosed space amid the rubble in almost complete darkness. Rescuers cut a hole in the concrete using a sledgehammer, and one by one the group was able to crawl free.

After the September 2010 quake, several tenants were convinced something was not quite right. Helen Guiney, who worked for Perpetual Trust on the first floor, told the Commission she was immediately struck by the large cracks in the central tower. The cracks grew and multiplied with each aftershock. 'After Boxing Day, I felt that the building definitely shook and creaked more during the aftershocks.'

The commissioners found that on February 22, 2011, the east–west shaking was 'appreciably greater' than the north–south shaking, and 'failure of the eastern wall initiated the collapse'. They noted there were 'considerably more' structural walls on the ground floor, but stopped short of endorsing two assessments of the cause of the collapse — one by the Department of Building and Housing and one by engineering firm Beca — that the eastern wall gave way just above this, between levels one and two.

The Commission's report listed six structural weaknesses, giving weight to Professor Nigel Priestley's observation during the hearing that the PGC was 'not a happy building'. One of the weaknesses was a lack of strength in the perimeter columns. When the shear wall failed in the quake, the columns on the east side bore the brunt of the pressure. They collapsed and the building came down.

This problem had been picked up in 1997 when a Holmes Consulting Group engineer noted that 'the potential failure of the columns is a life-safety issue as it could result in the loss of support and consequential collapse of all or part of the building'. Steel props were installed behind the columns a year later, which 'partially overcame' the problem, the report said, but another problem identified by the Holmes engineer, that the shear walls would likely 'rock' in only a moderate quake, went unaddressed.

By 2007, the building's age meant the Christchurch City Council's new quake-prone building policy came into play when upgrades were considered, but an assessment by Holmes that the building should perform 'reasonably well' in a quake satisfied this.

The building was inspected five times between the September 2010 and February 2011 quakes — four times by Holmes engineers — and declared safe each time.

Small cracks in old buildings, like those found by the Holmes engineers at the PGC building, could be wrongly interpreted as insignificant, the Commission's report said: 'The reinforcement crossing the crack might have either extensively yielded or completely failed at the crack. After the earthquake the crack, which might have opened to an appreciable width during the earthquake, might close.

'This indicates that the visual inspection procedures after an earthquake for buildings such as the PGC building need to be reviewed.'

**TOP** Department of Building and Housing deputy chief executive, sector policy, Suzanne Townsend appeared before the Royal Commission on November 9, 2011.
**STACY SQUIRES**

**BOTTOM** After the September 2010 earthquake, red stickers began popping up on the windows and doors of buildings in the city centre, including on this Thai restaurant in Victoria St.
**IAIN MCGREGOR**

**ALL OF THE** estimated 3867 unreinforced masonry buildings in New Zealand are considered earthquake-prone. The Commission's review covered the failure of 21 buildings in the February 2011 earthquake, which together had resulted in 42 deaths.

Department of Building and Housing officials admitted at the Commission hearings that quake-prone buildings had not been a priority before the Canterbury quakes. The department's sector-policy deputy chief executive Suzanne Townsend conceded there were gaps between best practice and what was allowed under the law. 'It is not something that people have as a priority asked us to change up until now,' she said.

Much of the evidence to the Commission came from earthquake engineers. Some argued for radical reform of the regime for strengthening quake-prone buildings. Several engineers, including two experts from the United States,

criticised the fact that most of the decision-making was left to local councils, arguing that tougher national standards were needed. They presented as evidence Building and Housing Department figures showing that of the 72 local councils in New Zealand, 23 took an entirely 'passive' approach to quake-strengthening old buildings.

Even councils that took an 'active' approach often gave owners decades before requiring them to fix anything, the engineers told the Commission. Owners were given an average of up to 21 years to strengthen old buildings. Twenty-eight councils had no deadlines at all, the evidence presented by the engineers showed.

Under the Building Act, old buildings are required to be strengthened to one-third — or 33 per cent — of the standard for new buildings. Wellington engineer Adam Thornton told the Commission that using a percentage of the new building standard led to widely varying results in strengthening old buildings. 'I think it's fair to say both the regulators and designers feel it is quite ambiguous.'

Before September 4, 2010, the Christchurch City Council's policy gave some owners up to the year 2042 to strengthen their buildings. Mayor Bob Parker told the Commission the prohibitive cost was the main reason requirements were not more strict. Strengthening costs for about 500 buildings were estimated at $200 million.

'It's not hard to see the overall total potentially facing our city would have been in excess of $1 billion. This is a problem that faces the whole country in terms of risk,' Parker said.

Council resource consents and building policy manager Steve McCarthy told the commissioners work had been ongoing since 2006 to measure the financial implications. 'The council was concerned they didn't have the full economic impact statement. They didn't know what the true cost [to the city] was.

'I think it was always council's intention to set time frames and be active in this space, but they didn't feel they had sufficient information at that time.'

The Commission's report, released in December 2012, announced 36 sweeping proposals for earthquake-prone buildings throughout New Zealand. It recommended that commercial, public and multi-storey, and multi-unit residential buildings, be brought up to minimum standard within 15 years, down from the current average of 28 years. Buildings with unreinforced masonry would be assessed within two years and strengthened or demolished within seven. Local authorities would be given authority to force homeowners to repair hazards such as unreinforced chimneys.

Not all the recommendations were backed by the government, which pushed instead for a 15-year time frame for all quake-prone buildings. Some

Cantabrians who had been badly hurt or affected by the earthquakes were disappointed. Bev Edwards, who was paralysed when the building she was in collapsed in the February quake, said 15 years was 'a very long time, especially if we continue to have earthquakes'.

Robert Gilbert, who lost his 22-year-old son Jaime when the Iconic Bar collapsed on the corner of Manchester and Gloucester streets, said the more lenient time frames were 'appalling'.

CHRISTCHURCH CITY COUNCIL came under intense scrutiny for its post-earthquake procedures, especially the thoroughness of rapid assessments, decisions made over reopening buildings, protective fencing, following up make-safe notices and confusion over the coloured placard system for assessments.

An internal debriefing on building evaluations made after the September 2010 quake found the council had not grasped the magnitude of the job. After the Boxing Day shake in 2010, the council appeared to put the economic recovery over safety, it was reported. The council team responsible for evaluating dangerous buildings when the state of emergency was lifted after the September 4 quake — the building evaluation transition (BET) team — had been underresourced and overworked. The report, written by Esther Griffiths of Sisirc Consulting and Dean McNulty of McNulty Engineering Management, was made public only after the Commission demanded it be submitted as evidence. The two consultants were also involved in establishing or running the BET team, with Griffiths the project manager.

Mayor Bob Parker said before the Commission hearings that the council and other agencies had responded 'incredibly well' to the September and Boxing Day quakes in 2010. 'Collectively, I think we did a very good job. I'm not saying it was perfect, and there are things we could have done better.' Parker said that after the Boxing Day 2010 quake, staff had faced pressure from businesses eager to reopen, but they had put safety first.

The Commission found that despite some problems, the evaluation operations after the quakes were well delivered. 'We consider that, overall, New Zealand was very well served by the engineers, building control officials and others who volunteered in the building safety evaluation process carried out after the Canterbury earthquakes.'

The commissioners described the system and skills as 'adequate', but said there was a 'significant gap' in respect of those buildings whose rapid assessment resulted in a green placard. All buildings should be assessed further after the rapid assessment phase of the operation, based on the nature of the event, the type of structure and the level of damage observed, they said.

THE SQUARE AND THE CENTRAL CBD – BEFORE THE EARTHQUAKES

# THE SQUARE AND THE CENTRAL CBD – AFTER THE EARTHQUAKES

1 Anthony Harper  2 Farmers carpark  3 MFL  4 Rural Bank  5 Pricewaterhouse  6 Warners  7 The Press

CHRISTCHURCH CENTRAL CITY – TAKEN BEFORE DEMOLITION

① Radio Network House ② Iconic Bar ③ SBS House ④ State Insurance ⑤ Grand Chancellor ⑥ Westpac ⑦ BNZ ⑧ Clarendon Tower

① Balu Network House  ② Iconic Bar  ③ SBS House  ④ State Insurance  ⑤ Grand Chancellor  ⑥ Westpac  ⑦ BNZ  ⑧ Clarendon Tower

The Ministry of Business, Innovation and Employment should also progress its proposal to establish a core team of building safety evaluators that the ministry could call on. The Commission also recommended a colour change from green to white for the placards, which were part of an internationally recognised system used in post-quake building checks. The placards were the result of rapid, damage-based checks, and advised building owners to seek a more detailed assessment.

**WITH THE CANTERBURY** earthquakes costing an estimated $30 billion, debate has raged over whether new building standards should be raised in the rebuild. All but two buildings — Canterbury Television and Pyne Gould Corporation — performed at least satisfactorily, but hundreds were damaged beyond repair and demolished.

Academics, senior practising engineers and professional engineering organisations were invited to debate building-design philosophies, such as life safety versus building survivability, and associated economic impacts at the Commission hearings.

Rajesh Dhakel, an associate professor in civil and natural resources

The Pyne Gould Corporation (PGC) building at 223 Cambridge Tce was built in 1966 and collapsed in the February 22 quake, killing 18 people. The Royal Commission concluded its design meant it was doomed for failure in a strong earthquake.

**STACY SQUIRES**

engineering at the University of Canterbury, said at the hearings that new design standards should go further than just protecting life because of the cost of the quakes. Soil testing and technology designed to minimise structural and non-structural damage to buildings should be among the new requirements.

'The design scheme which we have been applying now works well in achieving life-safety criteria, but it doesn't work well against minimising the [financial] loss,' Dhakel said. If quake-induced loss was minimised, safety and other design criteria would 'automatically be taken care of'. Although the performance of Christchurch's buildings in the quake exceeded expectations, Dhakel queried if that was enough.

Structural engineer Richard Sharpe, of Beca in Wellington, said buildings were never earthquake-proof. 'I believe our design philosophies acknowledge that there's always a chance that a properly designed, properly constructed structure will still collapse in an earthquake,' he said. New Zealand's seismicity model, which mapped quake risk around the country, was 'world-leading', but uncertainty still existed.

Trevor Kelly, of Holmes Consulting Group, gave a presentation on base isolation, a design method that allows a building to move on its base and absorb ground shaking. The technology, which he likened to a vehicle's suspension, was used in Wellington's Te Papa and Christchurch Women's Hospital. It is also popular in quake-prone Japan. However, its drawbacks include cost, the space needed for building movement and its unsuitability on soft soil, Kelly said.

Another low-damage design discussed was precast seismic structural systems (Presss), which allow controlled rocking of a structure's joints. Engineering company Structex designed the endoscopy unit at Christchurch's Southern Cross Hospital using Presss technology. Director Gary Haverland told the commissioners the building, completed in August 2010, used precast concrete walls and post-tensioned frames. The build was $30,000 under the $7.2 million budget and was completed ahead of schedule.

Structural engineer John Hare, of Holmes Consulting Group, said new building technology was 'well established but not well used'. Holmes had designed six buildings using base isolation, at a rate of one about every five years. The existing technology 'hasn't really let us down', Hare said. 'If a building was regular, well conceived, well detailed, well constructed and on good ground, by and large it's performed very well even though it's been through loads potentially up to twice what they were designed for.'

Des Bull, a professor of civil and natural resources engineering at Canterbury University, told the Commission design changes were needed. Damage to building connections could not be repaired in most cases and resulted in demolition, he said. The effect was like bending a paperclip until it snapped.

'They might be able to survive a subsequent series of smaller aftershocks, but could they survive another major event in the next 20 or 30 years? Highly unlikely, and that's some of the reasons these buildings have been brought down. They have nothing left in them to resist big earthquakes and are too expensive to repair,' Bull said.

In their final report, the commissioners noted that there was a place for the use of new building techniques in the Christchurch rebuild and that research should continue into the development of low-damage technologies. 'There will be many cases where their use is justified because of better structural performance, notwithstanding any increased costs that result,' they said.

The commissioners recommended the Department of Building and Housing foster greater communication and knowledge of the development of low-damage technologies among building owners, designers, building consent authorities, and the public.


**AS SILT, MUD** and water sloshed through the living rooms of thousands of newly built houses after the September 4 quake and the largest aftershocks, few homeowners were aware of what Canterbury councils had known about the risks to the land below.

More than 6500 properties were written off after the quakes because the land they were on was deemed prone to liquefaction and too damaged to be habitable. New subdivisions that were developed after the risks had been identified — such as Pacific Park in Bexley and Seafield Lagoon in Brooklands — were hit hard by the September 4 quake. The ground liquefied, badly damaging homes, and land was later red-zoned.

The Commission found 'weaknesses' in the process Environment Canterbury (ECan) and the Christchurch City Council followed when zoning land for redevelopment and approving consents for subdivision. The process was, however, 'sufficient to meet legislative requirements historically applicable'.

The weaknesses included a lack of compelling earthquake risk advice before the early to mid-1990s and a lack of council pressure on developers to investigate the geotechnical risks associated with their plans.

'We considered it would be inappropriate to ignore entirely the fact there has been unnecessary damage and costs sustained as a result of the development of land subject to a risk of liquefaction without duly considering that risk,' the commissioners said.

In their report they said it was incumbent on the city council to consider and manage the earthquake risk involved in any new subdivision or development, regardless of earlier zoning decisions.

'Where appropriate, applicants should have been required to undertake geotechnical investigations or other hazard assessment and if, as a result of those inquiries, risk was found to be present, mitigation actions should have been identified and monitored.'

The Resource Management Act should more explicitly acknowledge the potential effects of earthquakes and liquefaction, the Commissioners said.

—

*The Resource Management Act should more explicitly acknowledge the potential effects of earthquakes and liquefaction, the Commissioners said.*

—

A government report released in 2011 found that about 1200 Christchurch and Kaiapoi sections that were badly affected by liquefaction had clearly been identified as liquefaction-prone from the early 1990s.

City council resource consents and building policy manager Steve McCarthy later said the approach was 'universal' in New Zealand at that time. 'Our city plan placed reliance on building construction standards to manage earthquake risk for foundation design for new developments, rather than on the Resource Management Act (RMA) consenting processes.'

A report from resource management consultancy Enfocus to the Royal Commission said the council's plans appeared to strongly emphasise the risk of earthquakes but this did not translate into demands on developers. With one exception, ECan also did not push for quake-related conditions on developments, viewing its role as more educational. The Enfocus report did not solely blame the councils, saying the rules made it unclear how much weight should be given to the risk of quakes.

McCarthy said consents for new Christchurch development, where zoning changed from rural to residential, now required a geotechnical report that certified the land was the equivalent of Technical Category 1 or 2, not requiring the special foundations needed for construction on Technical Category 3 land. This report was required before section titles could be issued.

**THE ROYAL COMMISSION** inquiry was a lengthy and at times painful and adversarial process, but the findings will at least ensure many of the past mistakes will not be repeated. ■

# GERALD SHIRTCLIFF

## A LIFE BASED ON LIES

*Martin van Beynen*

When Gerald Morton Shirtcliff, 67, appeared before the
Canterbury Earthquakes Royal Commission on August 8, 2012,
he already had a shadow hanging over him.

**LEFT** Police and office workers try to extinguish the fire and rescue people trapped in the collapsed CTV building following the February 22, 2011 earthquake. Gerald Shirtcliff supervised the building's construction.

**CARYS MONTEATH**

**ABOVE** Michael Brooks, a former manager of Williams Construction, gives evidence at the Canterbury Earthquake Royal Commission hearings in August 2012 about the building of the CTV office block.

**DEAN KOZANIC**

**THE COMMISSION HEADED** by Justice Mark Cooper was hearing evidence on why the CTV building had collapsed on February 22, 2011, during the 6.3 magnitude earthquake. Of the people in the building, 115 were killed, although many did not die instantly. At least one person was still alive 12 hours after the collapse, with several others close by also surviving the initial collapse. These people were able to communicate with rescuers but died during the rescue efforts. Some of those who made it out of the building emerged relatively unscathed, while others lost limbs, and still others had severe injuries.

By August 8, counsel had already told the Commission that Shirtcliff had been initially unwilling to give evidence, and had only very recently asked for the professional reports into the collapse of the building. He was a vital witness because he had supervised the construction of the building, which later analysis showed had several serious defects. Michael Brooks, the managing director of the company that constructed the main structural part of the building, took the stand before Shirtcliff. Brooks told the Commission the fact a major concrete beam was not connected to the outside walls at each end of the building was 'extremely serious'. He also told the Commission he had hired Shirtcliff for his structural engineering background but had found 'he was not up to the job'.

By the time Shirtcliff began his evidence via a video link from Brisbane, *The Press* had already disclosed that he had been sentenced to 20 months' jail in 2005 for a Christchurch fraud in which he forged GST receipts to make it look like his failing automotive business was thriving. A Christchurch family was cheated of about $300,000 in the fraud.

As a consequence of the previous coverage, Shirtcliff's testimony was always going to attract a lot of interest. In a written statement

to the Commission he said he was 'not involved' in the construction of the building, but under questioning agreed he visited the construction site about once a week, relying mainly on the foreman to oversee the job.

He gave few personal details, but said he was a 'graduate civil engineer'. Although he was known in New Zealand as Gerald Shirtcliff, he had changed his name to William Fisher by deed poll in Australia about 40 years earlier, he said. He also revealed he had worked in South Africa in a supervisory role on construction projects.

It will never be known if the construction defects in the CTV building and the catastrophe of February 22 might have been avoided if Shirtcliff had been more attentive. But an investigation by *The Press* soon showed Shirtcliff was being less than honest with the Commission. It turned out his whole life was based on lies.

Shirtcliff had lived off and on in Australia since about 1970 under the name William Anthony Fisher, a name he had not in fact picked out of the blue. In 1968 and 1969 the young Shirtcliff had worked with an English engineer called William Anthony Fisher in Pretoria, South Africa, where they were both employed by the engineering firm Van Niekerk, Klein and Edwards. Fisher was a young engineer fresh out of university and Shirtcliff was employed as a technical assistant.

When Shirtcliff left South Africa toward the end of 1969 to settle in Sydney he took on Fisher's identity, including his birthplace, birth date,

Fraudster Gerald Shirtcliff eventually agreed to give evidence at the hearings. On August 8, 2012 he appeared via video link from Australia and answered questions about the CTV building and his former role as construction manager with Williams Construction.

**DEAN KOZANIC**

and his Bachelor of Engineering degree from the University of Sheffield. Shirtcliff then used the real Will Fisher's BEng to gain entry into a masters programme at the University of New South Wales (UNSW) in 1971, and also to become a member of the Australian Institute of Engineers in 1972. As 'Will Fisher' he was awarded a Master of Engineering Science in Highway Engineering in April 1974.

He later worked as an engineer for a Sydney firm, then called MacDonald, Wagner and Priddle (to become Connell Wagner and later Aurecon), before returning to New Zealand in the mid-1980s to work under his Shirtcliff name. In New Zealand he purported to be a 'registered' engineer and at one time a 'chartered' engineer.

While in Australia, Shirtcliff had used his Fisher identity on company documents and also to try to avoid extradition to New Zealand to face the fraud allegations. He spent a week in a Brisbane jail in 2003 before conceding he was actually Gerald Shirtcliff.

The real Will Fisher, now living in retirement in England after a career as a civil and structural engineer, said he was shocked and 'still reeling' after *The Press* contacted him to inform him about the theft of his identity. He wonders how many buildings, especially in Australia, have his name on them.

Fisher was awarded a BEng in 1967 after three years' study at Sheffield University. During the three years it took him to gain his degree, Shirtcliff was still in New Zealand.

The real Will Fisher says he was born in Hong Kong in 1946 (Shirtcliff was born in Wellington in 1945).

Fisher, who became a chartered engineer in London in 1974, remembers Shirtcliff as a colourful and somewhat mysterious character who told lots of stories. He says Shirtcliff was employed as a 'junior technician' in Van Niekerk, Klein and Edwards' design office, and he has no memory of him ever supervising a construction project.

'I joined VKE in February 1968 and left in July 1969 to return to England to get married,' Fisher says. 'We shared a flat over the last six to eight months of that period. Gerald was still in Pretoria when I left and I have had no contact with him since.'

Shirtcliff stuck to his guns about his bona fides right to the end. He did not want to talk to *The Press* when approached at his Brisbane home in August 2012. *The Press* later attended a meeting with his lawyer, David Tucker, and Shirtcliff, on advice, declined to answer questions. In subsequent correspondence through his lawyer, Shirtcliff continued to maintain he had an engineering degree from Sheffield University. He denied misleading the Commission, and said he had changed his name by deed poll in Australia 40 years ago. The change was prompted by a family rift, he claimed.

Shirtcliff categorically denied any of the wrongdoing claimed or suggested by *The Press* and threatened to sue the newspaper if it published the allegations. He gave *The Press* the name of a professor, Brian Shackel, at the UNSW whom he claimed had known him at Sheffield University and at UNSW. Shackel, however, subsequently told *The Press* he had no recollection of Shirtcliff or Fisher at either Sheffield or UNSW. He also said Shirtcliff had rung his wife a number of times in recent days trying to make contact.

At the time *The Press* tried to interview Shirtcliff in Brisbane, he was employed as a contractor by the global engineering consultancy WorleyParsons at its headquarters in the city. He had worked there since 2009.

Information provided by *The Press* to WorleyParsons prompted the firm to launch an immediate investigation, which led to the 'termination of [Shirtcliff's] relationship with the company'. All his work was being reviewed, the firm said.

After his departure from WorleyParsons, Shirtcliff almost immediately joined Sedgman, another international engineering firm, in Brisbane, working as an independent contractor. On learning about the allegations made by *The Press*, Sedgman commenced its own investigation and Shirtcliff left the firm almost immediately.

IT'S TEMPTING TO think Shirtcliff's unravelling started with his evidence to the Royal Commission. But he must have known his lies made him very vulnerable when the earthquake destroyed the CTV building. He must have realised his past was about to catch up with him.

In 2007, after serving his sentence for the fraud charges, all but two weeks of it on home detention, Shirtcliff had returned to Brisbane and built a comfortable lifestyle. His $200,000, 13-metre motor cruiser *Vagabond* bobs on the sunny water of beautiful Manly Boat Harbour. His home, only a stroll from the picturesque Cleveland coastline, is spacious and comfortable. A late-model white Mercedes shares the double garage with his wife's new Citroën.

He was a husband, father, grandfather and respected professional, still working in his mid-sixties. Not bad for someone who secretly had a serious fraud conviction and a stolen identity. In Brisbane, only his family appeared to know him as Gerald Shirtcliff. To others he was Will Fisher, a university-educated engineer with a CV that would make any professional man blush with pride.

He was born Gerald Morton Shirtcliff in 1945, the third-born and first son of a respected Wellington family. His father Morton, a business executive, would end his career as the South Island manager for Shell Oil.

TOP *The Press* travelled to Brisbane in August 2012 to track down Gerald Shirtcliff and get some answers about his involvement in the construction of the CTV building. He lives in a spacious home at Victoria Point, a stroll from the picturesque Cleveland coast, with a late-model Mercedes and a new Citroën in the garage.
**KIRK HARGREAVES**

MIDDLE Shirtcliff was employed as a contractor by the international engineering consultancy WorleyParsons in downtown Brisbane.
**KIRK HARGREAVES**

BOTTOM Shirtcliff's $A200,000, 13-metre motor cruiser *Vagabond* at berth in Manly Boat Harbour.
**KIRK HARGREAVES**

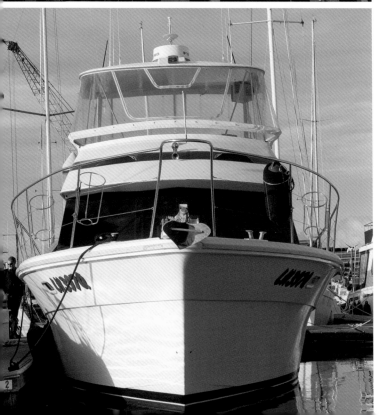

Gerald, who was a choir boy, was bright but did not thrive academically at Rongotai College. He left school to work in a Wellington bank and then an insurance company. Associates of the time say he had a proclivity for telling lies. He joined the Territorial Army as a bandsman, playing the cornet or trumpet.

His early jobs did not work out, and he left to train for his commercial pilot's licence at the Wanganui Flying School. His father was a competent pilot and often took his children with him on flights. The Civil Aviation Authority has confirmed that Gerald Shirtcliff held a commercial pilot's licence (Instrument Class 1 and aircraft types, Group E, Cessna 336, Beech58P) between 1967 and 1990.

After his early failures, Shirtcliff's father, thinking some overseas experience might straighten out his wayward son, organised a job for him at Niekerks in Pretoria. His friend Piet van Zyl, also a pilot, was a partner in the firm. Shirtcliff landed in Pretoria in 1968. According to his own version of events, he rose quickly through the ranks and was soon supervising construction projects and, with a new 'airline transport' rating, flying staff to remote locations in the company aircraft.

An associate of the time, South African engineer Niek Diedericks, has a different recall. He says he and Shirtcliff were employed as technical assistants with no supervisory responsibilities. Diedericks claims Shirtcliff told him he was escaping the Vietnam War draft in New Zealand (in fact, New Zealand did not have a draft for Vietnam) and he cannot remember Shirtcliff doing any flying. Although some partners had their own aircraft, the South African branch of the firm did not, he says.

The two also knocked around with the young engineer William Anthony Fisher, who had recently graduated from the University of

Sheffield with a top Bachelor of Engineering degree. They went camping and drinking together, and enjoyed the social life Pretoria had to offer.

Will Fisher says Shirtcliff was good company, but he was disturbed by the lies Shirtcliff told, apparently to escape an arranged marriage in New Zealand. 'We flatted together for about eight months. He was good fun to be with. Lots of quips and jokes. He was very much his own man, doing what he wanted to do,' Fisher says.

He describes Shirtcliff as 'pretty bright'. 'He was always keen to learn how things were done.'

Diedericks claims Shirtcliff left the firm under a cloud, after an incident in which Shirtcliff allegedly forged Piet van Zyl's signature on a cheque and cashed it. Late in 1969, Shirtcliff left South Africa for Sydney, Australia, ready to start afresh. So fresh, in fact, that he had a new name. It had a familiar ring: William Anthony Fisher.

Shirtcliff would later claim he changed his name to disassociate himself from his family, due to abuse by his father. But as we have seen, he assumed much more than just Fisher's name, and for a man who wanted nothing to do with his family, especially his father, he was surprisingly willing to ask for his father's help with his masters project. Morton Shirtcliff was well versed in roading surfaces and bitumen from his stint as bitumen manager for Shell Oil in New Zealand.

After gaining his Masters of Engineering in the name of William Fisher, Shirtcliff worked for a short time as a project manager in Sydney, including on a 33-storey building in Kings Cross. He also worked as a fleet manager for Streets Ice Cream before joining MacDonald, Wagner and Priddle, where he met his wife Julie. By the mid-1980s, he and his family were on the move again, this time landing in Christchurch.

The move, he would say later, was an attempt at a family reconciliation, but sources close to the family say that is misleading and it was more likely he was escaping trouble in Sydney. In any event, the family reverted to the name Shirtcliff.

One day at Christchurch Airport Shirtcliff met Murray Cresswell, a commercial pilot with ideas of setting up a regional airline. Shirtcliff expressed immediate interest, maintaining he had money to invest from a stint as a nuclear engineer in South Africa, Cresswell claims. Shirtcliff, he says, also asserted he was a top pilot.

Shirtcliff took a management role in the company, Goldfields Air, and convinced the other stakeholders that his plans for the company, which operated a seven-seater Piper Navajo previously used by the Victorian state premier, would lead to success. The big plans seemed unrealistic to Cresswell and the two quickly fell out. Goldfields Air failed in 1986.

Cresswell wasn't impressed with Shirtcliff's ability as a pilot. He flew with him rarely, but says on one occasion Shirtcliff was about to fly into a 'reinforced cloud' (a mountain) before he corrected him. Cresswell claims the operation's chief pilot, Neil Abbott, told him Shirtcliff was unteachable.

After the airline debacle, Shirtcliff took a job with Williams Construction, the company contracted to build the CTV building. Williams was a public company that had been founded by Wellingtonian Arthur Williams (later Sir Arthur). It had a solid financial history, making it attractive to the many entrepreneurs out to make hay in the heady mid-1980s. The company had expanded rapidly, and managing director Michael Brooks was keen to add someone with structural engineering experience.

Tony Scott, a quantity surveyor for Williams, told *The Press* it was easy to scapegoat Shirtcliff, but if he had turned up regularly on the CTV site he might have prevented some of the construction mistakes highlighted in evidence before the Commission.

'If Gerald wasn't at the CTV site, what was he doing all that time?' Scott says.

Shirtcliff later continued as construction manager for a new company (Union Construction) set up by Scott and Brooks. Union took over the CTV job and the building was finished toward the end of 1987.

After both Williams and Union failed, Scott and Shirtcliff set up their own construction company (Shirtcliff Scott Ltd), with Shirtcliff looking after practical aspects on-site and Scott 'in charge of the office and finances'. Scott says the company did mainly design-and-build projects, including the huge Caxton Warehouse in Halswell and a five-storey apartment building in Park Tce.

'I have to say Gerald was generally capable and conscientious,' Scott says. 'He was a hard driver, and sometimes I would have to tell him this wasn't South Africa. He wasn't well liked.

'Although things turned sour at the end, we had a good partnership and didn't interfere with each other's jobs. I kept a tight control on the financial side of things.'

Scott saw the need for the new company to promote itself and encouraged Shirtcliff to put together a CV, which Scott then kept for 25 years and provided to the Royal Commission. In it Shirtcliff claims to have a BEng from the University of Sheffield, to have managed construction companies in New Zealand and overseas, to have experience managing an international company, and four years' corporate flying experience and management of a 'corporate flying division'.

'He did try to pull a couple of swifties on me, but nothing I couldn't handle,' says Scott, who also recalls some of Shirtcliff's interesting stories. Shirtcliff, he claims, said his father was the legal representative for Shell in

Britain and that was why he studied at the University of Sheffield. Shirtcliff also claimed to be an old boy of Christ's College, an elite private school in Christchurch.

After Shirtcliff Scott Ltd foundered, Shirtcliff set out on another venture based on an idea the company had bought from an American entrepreneur in Rangiora. 'Gerald took the idea and came around boasting how much money he was going to make and how he had got one over on me,' Scott says. 'I didn't care. I had much more important things to worry about.'

The idea involved setting up hamburger outlets in service stations. Thus, in October 1992, Autoburger Ltd was born. The company later changed its name to Langford Services, and went into liquidation in 1999.

During the 1990s, Shirtcliff also worked for March Construction as its in-house engineer. Owner Edwin March told *The Press* Shirtcliff worked for the company for about eight months in the early nineties on a sewage pipeline in Whanganui. March says he found out by chance that Shirtcliff was not registered as an engineer in New Zealand, and queried him. 'He told me he was registered in Australia under the Fisher name. He just did levels for us, things like that. There was no problem with his work. He did a good job for us.'

But this is not quite what March told the police in March 2003, as evidenced by a statement released by the police under the Official Information Act. In the statement, March said Shirtcliff had been the 'house' engineer for March in 1993–94, and again in 1998 when he was employed 'on and off' as a consultant. March told the police Shirtcliff had signed off an engineer's design certification on a sheet-pile wall at the Peterborough apartments in Christchurch, using the name Shirtcliff and giving a registration number.

Another engineering firm queried the certification. When confronted, Shirtcliff said he had used his Australian registration, which was under the name William Fisher, March told the police. 'He told me the reason for using another name was because his father had hated him, so he was brought up by his aunts in London and renamed,' the statement says.

Shirtcliff's next business venture was a Nationwide Service Centre franchise in St Asaph St in central Christchurch. The business was busy but not profitable, and by 1997 Shirtcliff was wanting out. But how to sell a failing business?

Eric and Kay Zust, a successful Queenstown business couple, originally from Switzerland, had their children in boarding school in Christchurch and wanted to move closer. They had run a thriving souvenir business but knew nothing about the automotive trade.

The initial negotiations stalled over the franchise agreement, but Shirtcliff contacted the couple again about a year later saying the business had experienced phenomenal growth, and produced the GST figures to

Tony Scott encouraged Gerald Shirtcliff to put together a CV when they set up Union Construction together. Scott kept a copy of that CV for 25 years and is seen here presenting it at the Royal Commission in August 2012.

DEAN KOZANIC

prove it. Zust thought he was onto a winner. Shirtcliff stayed on for two weeks to show him the ropes, then left quickly for Australia, taking all the vehicle records with him.

Zust smelt a rat, checked the previous GST returns actually provided to IRD, and found they were nothing like the ones Shirtcliff had shown him. 'I realised immediately the business would fail, but I didn't know how to get out of it,' he says.

Zust hung on for a year, paid all the business' creditors, and virtually gave the business to its employees. He also pursued Shirtcliff and, in December 2000, the High Court awarded the Zusts $640,000 in damages and costs. The Zusts also pressed the New Zealand police to act, and wrote to parliamentarians including the prime minister.

Shirtcliff was arrested in Brisbane in 2003, although he was adamant he was not Gerald Shirtcliff, despite a car in his driveway being registered in the name of his daughter Kate Shirtcliff.

After many twists and turns, Shirtcliff agreed to return to Christchurch to face charges. In 2005, he was found guilty of fraud and jailed for 20 months by Christchurch District Court judge Murray Abbott, who said Shirtcliff was 'grossly dishonest' and that his actions displayed 'patent criminality'.

Zust's victim impact statement said Shirtcliff had made a mockery of the New Zealand justice system. 'I believe in his vocabulary the words honesty and compassion have the meaning of stupidity. He is intelligent but also devious, calculating and cunning. I and my family will never recover what we lost or heal the emotional damage he has done to us.'

Shirtcliff was in jail for only two weeks before his lawyer got his sentence changed to home detention. Phil Stanley and Sue Lyons, who knew him from being fellow franchisees in the failed Nationwide network, agreed to take him in. Shirtcliff told them he was due a $900,000 pension from his time as a manager at a Ford plant in South Africa.

'He convinced us he was innocent. He had a lovely smile and came across as a kind grandfatherly type of guy. We could see he was a pretty sharp character but we sort of admired him,' Stanley says. The couple treated Shirtcliff like one of the family, and Lyons cooked and cleaned for him.

Shirtcliff stayed with them for 20 months.

At the time, Stanley owned another autoservice business in Sydenham, and Shirtcliff helped out in the business. 'He was an absolute master for charging for things he didn't fit,' Stanley says. 'I had to tell him that was not the way I operated.'

An inventor specialising in alternative fuels, Stanley had a Honda Civic running on ethanol by the time he was 27. While Shirtcliff was with them, he was testing a dual-fuel system for diesel engines that he had developed over a decade. A test engine in his workshop was running on four different fuels, and he would later get it running on cow effluent. Normally Stanley made interested parties sign a confidentiality agreement, but he trusted his friend Shirtcliff and spent a lot of time explaining the invention.

Lyons says Shirtcliff often talked about shouting them an Australian holiday for being so kind to him. 'He would say, "As soon as I get out of here you guys are coming over. I'm shouting you a holiday. We will go out on the boat."

'As soon as the bracelet was off, he [Shirtcliff] was off to the airport. No goodbye. No nothing.'

Shirtcliff resumed his life as Will Fisher in Brisbane, and told some wealthy investors he had an idea for a dual-fuel system. Brisbane contractor Wayne Smith paid him $1000 a week to develop the idea and get it working.

Only eight months after Shirtcliff left Christchurch, a company called DGC Industries, of which Shirtcliff's wife Julie Rook was a director and shareholder, filed a patent for a dual-fuel system for diesel engines. The inventor named on the document: Will Fisher.

Stanley did not know about the patent application until informed by *The Press* late in 2012. His initial reaction is unprintable.

'He is a lifetime cheat,' Stanley says in a calmer moment. 'He's done it to everybody. He has no compunction.'

The patent documents filed by Shirtcliff had changed the invention slightly but not much, Stanley says.

Ruby Bay, Nelson, couple Sue Lyons and Phil Stanley took Shirtcliff in when his two-week stint in jail in 2005 for fraud came to an end and his sentence was changed to home detention. When Shirtcliff returned to Brisbane he also took and patented an invention for a dual-fuel diesel engine, originally devised by Phil Stanley.

**MARTIN DE RUYTER**

**THROUGH HIS LAWYER,** Shirtcliff has denied all negative assertions contained in this chapter. He says he is a qualified engineer and has not done anything wrong. Although he refused to answer specific questions, he says he has worked hard and all he wants is to be left in peace to get on with his life.

It will be a life radically different from what it was before *The Press* investigation. Although the Royal Commission declined to reopen its inquiry to admit the new evidence about Shirtcliff, it is hard to see it ignoring the evidence.

*The Press* articles prompted both the UNSW and Engineers Australia to start their own investigations. The upshot was that the university stripped Shirtcliff of his masters degree and Engineers Australia terminated his membership.

Both the New Zealand and Australian police are investigating various aspects of his conduct, although no progress has been reported at the time of writing.

Shirtcliff now has no job and his reputation is in tatters.

None of it was necessary, says a close associate, who asked not to be named.

'He was bright enough and hard-working enough to have achieved it all honestly. It's such a waste, and he has done so much damage to his family, to others and to himself.' ∎

Temporary houses were built in several locations, including here in Linwood Park, to cope with demand for accommodation after the quakes. Pressure from people getting their homes repaired has made securing rental accommodation a nightmare, particularly for those with pets.

**KIRK HARGREAVES**

# HOUSING
## WINNERS AND LOSERS IN THE PROPERTY GAME

*Liz McDonald*

What does a red-zoned suburb sound like?

On a sunny Saturday afternoon in the summer of 2013 it sounds like just two things. Birds. And silence.

No squealing children on scooters. No lawnmowers. No cars.

Close your eyes and you could be in the countryside, not in a city with houses, fences and footpaths.

A front-end loader clears ground at Faringdon, a new $200-million subdivision in the Selwyn District at Rolleston which will create more than 1000 new sections and boost the town's population by several thousand people.

**KIRK HARGREAVES**

**WHILE THE RED-ZONE** residents have gone and nature is reclaiming what they had built, the reverse is happening in the city's outskirts and commuter towns. There, the sounds are of hammers and concrete mixers as rows of homes rise in new subdivisions to replace those too damaged to fix or in neighbourhoods now unfit to live in.

The green belt is becoming the commuter belt as the city finds room for the 20,000 new dwellings that are expected to be built by 2017. For the individuals involved this means a new home, a new community, a good dose of stress, and maybe some excitement. For the city it means another type of seismic shift.

This replacement of thousands of homes is not only vast in its scale and unprecedented in its urgency; it will significantly alter the make-up of the city's housing stock. The houses lost to the quakes were mostly a mix of pre-war timber, post-war brick and block, and modern monolithic cladding, reflecting their decade of origin and the refurbishment whims of subsequent owners. Modern no-nos such as south-facing living areas, isolated kitchens and zero insulation were surprisingly common in the more established suburbs.

Their replacements will be fully insulated, built to the sun, with modern kitchens, and more thoughtfully laid out for modern living. If they are in the bigger new subdivisions, their occupants may have access to cycle lanes, walking tracks and neighbourhood parks and shops. Today's economy,

The new Yaldhurst Village subdivision on the outskirts of Christchurch near the airport has changed traffic patterns and seen traffic lights installed on the main highway west beyond the current city limits.

**DEAN KOZANIC**

housing policies and design trends will determine the quality of these new houses. Many homeowners are trying to cut costs as they rebuild, choosing predesigned homes from cookie-cutter layouts on building company websites.

Luxuries such as internal-access garages and ensuite bathrooms now come as standard, and energy-saving features will please the pockets of new owners. But these houses will be built of pre-assembled components and manufactured materials rather than crafted from natural products, and will lack the character of the earlier styles they replace, such as villas, bungalows, art deco homes, post-war state homes and 1970s chic.

The new shape of the city will also affect how much cash will be spent on new housing. In the traditionally back-to-front Christchurch real estate market, where living near the sound of the waves is cheaper than being under a flight path, the east–west shift now under way costs buyers with each kilometre. This is compounded by the problem that a dollar in a long-established suburb does not go as far as a dollar in a newly laid out subdivision.

Land and development costs — including meeting today's tougher standards and paying councils the development levies they demand — make a new section a pricey commodity before you build so much as a fence on it. That may have worked when a new home in a fancy estate was a coveted lifestyle option for the well-heeled. But not when it is the only choice for red-zoners.

Land developers have quickly redrawn plans to meet the demand for

cheaper options — which can only mean smaller sections. They report that the smallest sites are their biggest sellers, with those covering 400 to 450 square metres in heavy demand. These are around half the size of family-home sections in the 1970s to early 2000s, and close to a third of the dimensions of the old-style quarter-acre.

A small section is a plus for lifestyle reasons if you'd rather play golf than mow the lawn, and the mixed-density choices on offer will please many. But that lack of space is a minus if you've got a family and are just desperate to cut costs. As well as less space for children to run and climb and hit a ball, it means less privacy from the neighbours and more noise.

These communities were first laid out with high-density housing intended for young couples, empty-nesters and single folk — not for families buying whatever they can afford. In future decades, these neighbourhoods will be less likely to look like slums if today's land and building prices have allowed for thoughtfully designed homes with a bit of space between them.

**UPSET THE DELICATE** balance of supply and demand that regulates the property market even a little and there's bound to be trouble. Unleash two years of seismic chaos, an insurance freeze and the loss of thousands of homes, and you have the Christchurch property market today.

Buying an existing home is the cheapest option for red-zoners, but there have not been enough to go around. The resulting imbalance in demand pushed up house prices by 10 per cent in the two years after the first big quake, and by Christmas 2012 the city's average house value topped

$400,000 for the first time. There was talk of multi-offers on houses, queues at open homes, and competitive bidding at auctions.

As insurance hurdles were lowered new house construction finally began, picking up in the spring of 2012. Canterbury Registered Master Builders Association president Clive Barrington described the upturn as a relief, and a turnaround from the 'pretty grim' situation a year earlier. But while it's a relief for the construction industry, the start is still a long way off the numbers of new homes the region needs.

Local valuer Bevan Fleming described the housing shortage as 'everywhere, right across the board'. He called the market for houses 'very strong', and did not see the inflation slowing until more homes were available.

*Unleash two years of seismic chaos, an insurance freeze and the loss of thousands of homes, and you have the Christchurch property market today.*

Housing affordability has been an issue in Christchurch since prices doubled during the housing boom of 2003 to 2008. Even before the earthquakes, a fall-off in house construction had begun strangling the nation's housing supply. The quakes pulled the noose tighter.

As well, the resulting hassles over insurance, repairs and land classification kept many Christchurch homes off the real estate market.

As these hurdles were slowly cleared and the market began picking up, one solution started to emerge — owners in less-damaged neighbourhoods were selling to red-zoners, taking advantage of rising prices and making the lifestyle switch to a new home. In some cases there was a domino effect of buyers and sellers progressively upgrading to bigger homes and better suburbs, with a shiny new home for the buyer at the end. The trend helped boost prices right across the market.

But the inflation could have been a lot worse for buyers. The staggered red-zoning of suburbs may have maddened orange-zoners, those stuck awaiting either the green light to repair or the red light to leave, as they sat watching prices escalate away from them. But at least it released residents into the market in batches and helped ward off a stampede. Other frustrations, such as delays in settling insurance claims, bans on new policies, wrangles over government payouts and slow progress on repairs, also had the silver lining of slowing the inflationary effect.

The concern now is what the incoming tide of rebuild workers will do to house prices. Statistics New Zealand's projections are for 50,000 extra people in the city by 2031 as migrant workers continue to pour in for rebuild jobs. More inflation is inevitable, even with temporary housing and promises of workers' camps.

Tenants have been in a worse situation. With the owners of damaged but fixable homes coming into the rental market alongside displaced tenants, rental properties have been in hot demand. As well, homes have been needed for temporary insurance staff, loss adjusters and demolition workers.

Rents have been rising as fast as 12 per cent a year in the city overall, and by even more in desirable spots. Most in demand have been family homes near schools in red-zoned neighbourhoods. Rentals under $250 a week have all but disappeared from the city. Suddenly landlords could be choosy, and less desirable tenants — especially those without jobs, tidy credit ratings or clean police records — found themselves out in the cold. Sometimes literally. Even the crime of owning a poodle or a tabby cat was enough to render families homeless.

A new market emerged — furnished short-term rentals for insurance policy holders sitting out repairs and for out-of-town workers being housed on the company chequebook. While these $1000-a-week homes were more a motel substitute than part of the standard rental market, their removal from the rental pool further increased the pressure. Temporary homes were built in parks, but only for residents of damaged homes. Housing New Zealand has new housing on the drawing board, but until it is built social agencies have been left to try and meet the housing needs of the most desperate.

Just before Christmas 2012, a second wave of rental demand hit, this time affecting the top and middle of the market. The early rebuild workers — managers of inbound businesses establishing a base in the city, and professionals such as quantity surveyors and structural engineers — began hunting for quality family homes in the $300,000 to $600,000 market. Even the top-end rentals flew off letting agents'

books. Agents are reporting vacancy rates of close to zero and have had to turn families away. And that's even before the bulk of the rebuild workers get off the plane.

**IN AMERICA THEY** call them 'exurbs', commuter towns beyond the suburbs where mortgages are met with city pay-packets. Canterbury traditionally had towns based on industrial or farming economies, such as Kaiapoi and Rangiora, and newer pockets of lifestyle blocks at places such as Ohoka and Prebbleton. There was no need for the exurb model in a city like Christchurch with plenty of land for all.

But the earthquakes changed that. With the western suburbs short on real estate and high on price, and titles for promised Christchurch sections still nowhere in sight, cash-strapped buyers from the eastern suburbs pushed out further and further to available and cheaper land. To Rolleston, Lincoln, Pegasus, Kaiapoi.

Waimakariri and Selwyn districts saw record house inflation of 12 per cent in one year, the highest in New Zealand, and together were issuing more consents for new homes than the city they surround. The towns are booming. Rolleston has a dozen new subdivisions and the population has tripled in size since 2006. New ratepayers in the towns will fund new amenities and infrastructure and create an internal-demand economy.

Residents in new subdivisions are adjusting not only to brand new homes and neighbourhoods, but to rules laid down by developers to maintain standards. So no old cars. No way-out house designs. No big dogs. Long term, these towns may go from strength to strength — unless future petrol price hikes send residents back to town, leaving depressed house prices and dwindling rating bases in their wake. The future of the towns may depend on whether they remain attractive, offering stimulating communities and popular amenities rather than just a haven from damaged land and city real estate prices.

At the opposite end of the spectrum of housing solutions is the plan for high- and medium-density housing complexes in central Christchurch. Fully aware of the country's traditional suburban housing model, the city council has already canvassed residents on whether they would consider shifting to such a precinct — and what they would want to find if they did. Are community spaces important to would-be residents? What about privacy? Car parking? Pets? Family-friendly homes? Buying or renting? If there was a choice between cost and space, which would be more important?

For many residents, such a move into the city's four avenues will probably depend not just on the look or price-tag of such a home. They will

**TOP** New homes under construction in Rolleston. The Selwyn District is growing rapidly as Christchurch families move out of town and head further down State Highway 1.
**DEAN KOZANIC**

**BOTTOM** Rolleston was touted as a satellite town of Christchurch in the early 1970s by Norman Kirk's Labour Government. Some 40 years later, and invigorated by the Canterbury quakes, that plan seems to be finally coming true.
**DEAN KOZANIC**

likely be waiting for the return of the amenities that are the main attraction of central-city living, and for a new central city to put them in.

**AT FIRST IT** sounded tidy, if a little unnerving. The government had tucked every occupied and flat Christchurch section into a folder labelled TC1, TC2 or TC3. These technical categories were intended as helpful guides to deal with the problem of repairing and rebuilding busted foundations. The higher the number, the more attention was needed.

But buyers, insurers and banks took the new labels to heart. Immediately, insurers put the most damage-prone TC3 sites in the too-risky basket. Banks disliked the idea of lending on them, and buyers had little choice but to avoid them. The authorities promised prompt foundation-design guidelines and site-specific drilling on the 28,000 affected properties.

In the meantime, prices shifted quickly, stratifying the market into layers like an abandoned milkshake. By spring 2012, state-owned valuation company Quotable Value had totted up the numbers. The average price differential between TC3 and TC1 homes, compared against rating valuations, was 15 per cent. Valuer Natalie Edwards commented that while statistics showed a small average drop in values, the reality for some owners was much worse. Individually she has seen 'huge variations', and some TC3 property owners' values have fallen by 50 per cent.

Fear and uncertainty has dealt a blow to the market for TC3 homes, and sites where such homes have been demolished became almost impossible to sell. As one real estate boss said, the government did not see that coming when they dreamed up their tidy classifications.

One class of buyer did emerge for TC3 land with written-off homes left standing. Every problem breeds an opportunity, and risk-tolerant buyers swooped on properties that were almost as cheap as bare land. Sellers with an insurance payout on a house that was too pricey to fix were happy to sell cheaply, and buyers got an almost free house they could rent out or occupy in a high-demand market. There would be no insurance, of course, but if the worst happened, the owners would still have a piece of land to rebuild on.

The number of sales of TC3 homes is rising slowly, but the need to discount means the price gap remains. Many owners are waiting for that price differential to close before considering putting a 'For Sale' sign on the lawn.

**DECIDING WHERE BEST** to build new homes in Christchurch had been exercising minds even before the earthquakes. With its location at the edge of a broad plain, the city should have been spoilt for choice for new land. But the coast to the east and the hills and harbour to the south were not the only barriers. To the north and west lie the city's water-supply aquifers and no-housing zones protecting the airport from noise-sensitive residents who could curtail its business.

Before the quakes the Christchurch City Council and the Selwyn and Waimakariri district councils had put their heads together and drawn a red line around the city, sketching go and no-go housing zones in what they called the Greater Christchurch Urban Development Strategy. The idea was to tidy the map and create efficiencies rather than, as one council put it, having contractors run around the countryside hooking up pipes at the whims of land developers. But developers whose sites fell outside the line did manage to successfully claw back some ground through the courts.

Then the earthquakes happened and Canterbury Earthquake Recovery Minister Gerry Brownlee hurriedly redrew the line to open up land for housing. He consulted the councils and the airport company first. They took the opportunity to suggest a housing line where they wanted it, making the most of the minister's extraordinary powers under the Earthquake Recovery Act and his ability to rule out subsequent Environment Court appeals.

Brownlee's redrawing of the boundary created more land for housing in future decades but ruled out other sites previously approved for development. The aggrieved developers took the minister to the High Court in what was the first legal challenge to his special powers. It shaped up in the courtroom like a battle of giants represented by high-priced lawyers. On one side there was the minister, backed by the city council, the Canterbury Regional Council, two district councils (Selwyn and Waimakariri), the

The end of Goodman St near Horseshoe Lake is deserted in this January 2012 photo. Time has now run out for the red-zoned residential area close to Burwood, which was badly affected by liquefaction in the big quakes.
**DEAN KOZANIC**

airport, the nation's richest iwi Ngai Tahu and developers who liked the new rules. On the other side were big land developers, including a major exporter and some high-profile investors and businessmen. Also joining the battle on opposite sides were the country's two big supermarket chains, which had plans to build supermarkets alongside new housing.

The court heard talk of backroom deals and secret emails, and allegations that the applicant developers had paid the price for politically motivated decisions. Years of debate over airport noise contours and land drainage were rehashed.

The judge came down in favour of the developers and set aside the minister's ruling, but the result has given the city little clarity over the question of where new houses will eventually go. Several follow-up claims on the subject have already gone to court, including the minister's unsuccessful appeal, and in early 2013 more hearings were in the pipeline.

While some of the development sites at the centre of the fight remain approved for housing, the rest remain in limbo. There is enough land for housing in the short term, but not for the years beyond. The protracted legal wranglings continue, Minister Brownlee has ordered a new local body land use recovery plan, and the developers and the city wait.

**LIKE THE ROLL** of the dice in a Monopoly game, the Canterbury earthquakes created winners and losers in the property market. Careful homeowners suddenly found themselves at the mercy of both the quakes and the authorities as their land turned to mud, or their suburb sprouted road cones and portaloos. Riverfront and hilltop locations quickly became more a liability than an attraction as the forces of nature waded uninvited into the housing market.

The stroke of a pen could wipe tens of thousands of dollars, or more, from the value of a citizen's biggest asset. Insurance and government payouts for red-zoners plugged some of the gap, but there were unhappy and unfair outcomes.

The losers were the uninsured, the underinsured, red-zoners with rating valuations considerably under market value, and others such as those in the middle of construction or a property deal. A government offer to pay half a property's rating value to the uninsured was lucky for those without cover on their homes, but unfair to those with uninsurable bare sections.

Valuers estimate that council rating values, a rough desktop calculation for rating purposes only, can vary from 50 per cent more to 50 per cent less than a home's value on the open market. Those with a high market value relative to rating value, like owners of well-kept, renovated older homes,

came out worse than those who had a lower market value but high rating value, such as neglected homes from recent decades.

For many, borrowing more cash was the only way to rehouse themselves.

The ability of red-zoners to split their payouts between the government and the Earthquake Commission also divided those communities into winners and losers. Red-zoners entitled to a rebuild could go replacement shopping with much bigger cheques than those paid out repair value on a house that was unable to be repaired. This disparity happened despite the inescapable fact that all were losing their homes.

The reshaped suburbs will also create winners and losers. Properties left bordering a reserve or waterway after neighbouring demolitions may suddenly gain value, while others near red zones will find the loss of amenities such as schools and shops detrimental to real estate prices. In most cases, those needing a rebuild will score a new house and tax-free capital gain. All over the city, people who would never have dreamt of choosing a house design from a catalogue will feel like Lotto winners.

Owners of less damaged homes also did well, gaining free redecorations because of hairline cracks and chipped tiles. Whole neighbourhoods face large-scale improvement as homes are replaced and repaired. However, owners with unusual, heritage, architecturally significant and even run-of-the-mill character homes have a fight on their hands if they don't want them replaced with modern boxes. At least one such owner has had a court ruling against his insurance company decided in his favour.

Landlords' fortunes also rolled with the dice. A rentable home in a market under pressure meant improved returns after years of flat rents in the city. A wrecked house stuck in insurance queues long after the rental insurance ran out

meant no income at all but a shiny new dwelling and rent to match at the end of it all.

**THERE'S A BIG** green opportunity out there, with the chance to boost the energy-efficiency quotient of some of the thousands of new Canterbury houses. Some developers and homeowners are seizing this opportunity. Buyers say they want it, some of them probably mean it, and a few of them may even be prepared to pay extra.

While better insulation and glazing will be building-code standard, the optional extra gaining the most popularity is the solar roof panel for either heating water or generating electricity (known as photovoltaic), or both. Modern technology has brought down the cost of home solar systems dramatically and they are cheaper to install new than to retrofit.

At the Highfield subdivision planned for the north side of Christchurch, developer Maxim Projects likes the idea so much it is putting solar systems on all 2200 homes. The result will be the country's biggest solar community. The systems will include both photovoltaic and hot-water panels, and will supply about a quarter of a typical home's energy needs. A deal with a local power retailer will enable residents to feed excess power into the national grid. The project was described by one commentator as one of the few rays of sunshine in the city's rebuild plans.

But how about the thousands of other homes that need to be rebuilt and repaired?

Christchurch architect Russell Devlin has called for homes to be built so that they are easier to repair in future quakes and also more sustainable. 'People understand they can build their houses better than they were before — they want them warmer and more comfortable.'

Devlin, whose own new home has a photovoltaic system supplying up to half its energy needs, says such a system is 'an investment better than putting money in the bank'. He believes architects are now doing better at designing buildings to survive large earthquakes as well as save lives, and that stronger foundations and better designs will minimise damage and make homes easier and cheaper to fix. 'This is an opportunity to raise the bar for the city's housing stock.'

The architect's comments echo what many residents of quake-torn Christchurch have said. The unprecedented repair and replacement of so many houses, and the creation of so many new subdivisions, is a great chance to get things right. To build well-planned communities with a heart. To build homes that are well thought out, affordable and efficient to run, comfortable and warm, and strong and safe. It is too good a chance to pass up. ∎

# NEW LIFE IN PEGASUS

For Steve and LeeAnn Christensen and their children Noah and Chloe, 2012 brought a happy housing outcome to their earthquake story. The couple were devastated when their riverside house in Shirley was damaged then red-zoned.

It was 'quite a big strain having to go through the insurance process', Steve said. 'We lost quite a bit of money but eventually they came to the party. It was a few stressful months, and then more earthquakes and not knowing if we were ever going to get out of that situation.'

They managed to rebuild in the new town of Pegasus, just north of Christchurch, moving into their new home in April 2012. Leaving their old community was a wrench, Christensen said, but they have settled into Pegasus alongside many other new arrivals. 'The roads are nice and straight, and there's no liquefaction or cracked roads or roadworks and it's safe and quiet. The children have made friends, there are lots of young families, and there are nice flat footpaths to ride their bikes on.'

They are enjoying the new house, too. 'We were in an old weatherboard house with air coming through the boards because it had moved and cracked. This is a nice new, warm house — it's quite a difference.'

The biggest downside is Steve's daily commute to his job in Christchurch, which takes 35 to 40 minutes rather than 10 from Shirley. They miss family being nearby, too, but LeeAnn's parents — red-zoned from their own home — are also rebuilding in Pegasus and will be handy for babysitting.

# GOODBYE TO A CHILDHOOD FRIEND

It's a plain enough little house, really: two bedrooms, stucco exterior, a drive running past the house — you know the sort of thing. But it has its charms. Big windows mean plenty of sun, and the roses thrive despite the sandy soil. Best of all, the beach is just one minute's walk away from the house on Rocking Horse Rd.

It is my childhood home and, like so many others in Christchurch, it is too damaged by the earthquakes to save. Like so many other families, we will be losing a repository of our collective memories to demolition.

I'm sure the rubble will make way for something sensible and well laid out, ideal for new occupants and for modern lifestyles. But that will be months or even years away. For now we say goodbye.

The back bedroom was where my sister Louise and I giggled long after lights out. In the kitchen, Mum taught us to make the perfect pavlova, and at the dining table Dad drilled us on the capital cities of Europe or the Ten Commandments. We loved the wide driveway where we rode our bikes and trikes, weaving slaloms under the carport. The lawn was ideal for cartwheels if you could steer clear of the cactus. The vacant sections all around were our playground, as were the sandhills where we built huts and the estuary where we splashed in the swimming hole.

The beach-house had a modest start even before our parents bought it in 1967. We heard it was brought in from Godley Head, where it had been a scout den or a military building or both, to be deposited on foundations that have proved to be its undoing. There was no insulation, no indoor–outdoor flow, no well-planned layout.

But our parents loved it and turned it into a family home. Straw matting gave way to carpets that had to be replaced every few years because of the sunshine and Dad's fondness for pacing. Mum sewed curtains, installed furniture from AJ White's and for some reason (probably uneven surfaces) wallpapered the ceilings.

The butterfly that adorned the front — my favourite feature when I moved in at the age of three — became a caterpillar again when it lost one wing in the *Wahine* storm of April 1968 and the other in the Big Blow of August 1975. Dad eventually conceded defeat and took the wingless insect down, with two of us holding the ladder steady while he muttered under his breath at the task.

The house was extended, first out the back to make more room for growing daughters, and later out the front to give my father a sunny sitting area during the ill health of his last years. We all loved the smell of the sea and the sunsets over the estuary. Mum hated the seagulls, though, because they dirtied her windows and dropped shellfish through the guttering.

In more recent years, the house made memories for a new generation — I brought my own children there often to be spoiled with Grandpa's favourite biscuits and Grandma's cuddles.

The house rebuilt on the site will grow new families and new memories for them. But by then the remains of our old home, like so many others, will be gone, buried deep in recycling heaps and landfills far away.

The new house may see PlayStations instead of cartwheels, and 21st-century chic instead of a butterfly on stucco, but there will still be laughter and teatime squabbles, and the beach across the road.

# HOUSE ON THE MOVE

The term 'moving house' had a literal meaning for one red-zoned Avonside family. Rather than lose their Edwardian villa, David Haywood and Jenny Hay, with their children Bob and Polly, simply picked it up and moved it to Dunsandel.

Sound simple? The reality turned out to be a lot more complicated than the idea. The project cost the Hay-Haywoods $100,000 plus 550 hours of planning and hands-on graft even before the move (Haywood described it as 550 hours of suffering in his rather amusing blog on the subject). Friends gave hours of back-breaking help.

Items including the garden pavers and the washing line had to be lifted and shifted, and the house carved up and reassembled at the other end. Even the roof had to come off to avoid hitting overhead power lines. Haywood, a writer and engineer, and Hay, a university lecturer, told *The Press* they made the decision for both financial and emotional reasons.

Their timber home boasts ornate fretwork, leadlight panels and generous fireplaces. 'We loved our house and it wasn't completely wrecked, so we wanted to save it by taking it with us,' Hay said.

The choice of location was complicated too.

They looked first for a section in Christchurch, but ran into the restrictive covenants subdivisions use to ban BYO houses. Isolated rural sites had their problems too, with their lack of services. So with the furniture in storage and the family in temporary housing, small-town Dunsandel got the nod and the house hit the road.

'It was pretty strange to see your house up on a truck like that, but great to see it arrive out in Dunsandel. We're thrilled,' Hay said. 'It was a lot more economical to move and fix our old house than to rebuild a completely new house. We're not going to come out of this thing too badly.'

While many red-zoners, mainly those with character homes, floated the prospect of 'shifting house', the Hay-Haywood family were among only a handful to follow through on the idea. The remaining houses, with their period architectural details, original materials and stores of memories, will be flattened.

The ultimate in mobile homes. In April 2012, the Edwardian house of David Haywood and Jenny Hay, pictured with their daughter Polly Haywood aged 14 months, at 336 Avonside Dr, was jacked up and shifted to its new location in Dunsandel. The family had searched in vain for a Christchurch section for their home.
JOSEPH JOHNSON

An Earthquake Commission
(EQC) inspector assesses a
Pines Beach house after the
September 4, 2010 quake.
ANDREW GORRIE

# INSURANCE
## AN INDUSTRY
## UNDER STRESS

*Michael Wright*

On September 4, 2010, the Earthquake Commission had 22
staff and only the odd television commercial to remind the
general public of its existence.

**WITHIN TWO WEEKS** of the 7.1 magnitude earthquake that struck Canterbury that day, staff numbers at the commission had ballooned to 600, including 155 estimators and 255 call centre operators. By November, the total number of staff had swelled to almost 1150.

That shake, and the catastrophic 6.3 magnitude quake that followed in February 2011, thrust public and private insurers into the Canterbury consciousness like never before. EQC would eventually employ, either directly or indirectly, 20,000 people and receive hundreds of thousands of claims for damage.

For many of us, how EQC and its private-sector counterparts carried out their duties was the defining issue of the quake recovery. Early reports after the September quake predicted that 100,000 households would make EQC claims, and that they would be worth about $1 billion. Previously, the biggest event EQC had had to deal with was the 1968 Inangahua earthquake, where it paid out on 10,500 claims.

Two years after the quake sequence started, the scale of what is by far the commission's largest-ever job was becoming clear. Its 2012 annual report put total liabilities at about $12.5 billion, with an estimated $800 million shortfall the government will have to cover. The private insurance bill is still vague, but thought to be in the vicinity of $20 billion.

The commission draws its funds through levies on homeowners' house insurance policies. Aside from those occasional television advertisements, the only other reminder people had of its existence was a line on their

**LEFT** Earthquake Commission staff packed into the main claims administration floor of their offices in November 2010.
**CARYS MONTEATH**

**MIDDLE** Broken crockery from the February 22, 2011 quake is swept up by Mohammed Ismail in his damaged Cashmere home.
**FIONA GOODALL**

**RIGHT** On July 19, 2011, EQC carried out its 100,000th assessment since the quakes began. St Albans homeowner Suzanne Oliver discusses quake damage with loss adjuster Terry Keating, centre, and estimator Jeremy Cosgrove.
**STACY SQUIRES**

insurance premium notices. Few could claim to have a detailed knowledge
of how the organisation worked.

Briefly, EQC covers the first $100,000 of damage to an insured property
for an earthquake event, $20,000 worth of contents damage, and $200,000
in land damage. House and contents damage above this is referred to private
insurers. Claimants with damage under $10,000, a threshold later upped to
$15,000, received cash payouts to handle repairs themselves, and those with
up to $100,000 worth came under a managed repair scheme.

**THE UNPRECEDENTED SCALE** of the September and February quakes soon started
to blur the recovery effort of insurers. As early as September 18, 2010, *The
Press* recorded that tempers were beginning to fray as the commission
struggled to cope with the volume of claims. So began a fraught relationship
between EQC, insurance companies and their customers.

With so many properties to assess, mistakes and delays were bound to
happen, but the trickle of unhappy homeowners soon became a torrent. Slow
response times and a lack of information, issues that would dog public and
private insurers, were the key complaints. EQC would concede throughout
the recovery that its communications could be better, but despite measures
to improve things it continued to generate disastrous headlines. Customers
complained of contradictory information, delayed information or, if a call-
centre operator couldn't find their record, no information at all.

EQC customer services general manager Bruce Emson acknowledged in April 2012 that the commission still had communication problems. 'The organisation is a very large, and at the moment a pretty disaggregated, one,' he said.

Improvements had included opening a claims processing office in Hamilton, relocating a Brisbane-based call centre to New Zealand, and setting up a mediation process for complaints. However, by then many people had already formed their opinions about the commission. Half the respondents to a survey published in *The Press* on the second anniversary of the September 2010 quake said they were dissatisfied with EQC's performance. EQC Canterbury events manager Reid Stiven admitted that the numbers were not good enough, and that the commission's internal polling was just as bad.

Australian connections provided another public-relations problem. As well as the Brisbane-based call centre, there was the hiring of a number of Australian ex-policemen to work as assessors. People with no loss-adjusting experience were contracted, primarily through private investigation firm Verifact, to inspect quake-damaged properties, mainly because of their administrative and people skills.

'To train someone to identify earthquake damage is not that difficult,' acting claims manager Barry Searle told *The Press* at the time.

The reaction to the foreign recruitment prompted a concerted effort to hire Kiwis 'for a number of reasons', Searle said in an email to a former

**LEFT** EQC customer services general manager Bruce Emson met with the Christchurch City Council in August 2012 to explain the commission's progress and its priorities for repairs.
**STACY SQUIRES**

**RIGHT** EQC Canterbury events manager Reid Stiven admitted under pressure that too many people were dissatisfied with the commission's performance and that it was not good enough.
**JOHN KIRK-ANDERSON**

police officer, 'not the least of which is public perception'.

Assessors' starting pay rates of $75 an hour plus accommodation and other benefits also raised the eyebrows of those on the outside looking in, and led to claims that quake assessment was a gravy train for those who knew the right people. Soon it emerged that some of those people were family members of senior commission staff.

A series of *Press* stories revealed that the sons of three senior staff were working in assessment teams, and the daughter of a fourth was one of two EQC staffers who started a building company for quake repairs while still working as an assessor and an estimator, prompting a conflict of interest investigation. Months after it was first flagged as a potential problem, the commission launched an independent review of its recruitment process which 'vindicated' its hiring and staff policies. All up, about 30 EQC management and field workers had close family relationships with other EQC staff, but the commission repeatedly refused to confirm facts or grant requests for interviews on the subject.

The assessments themselves created controversy, too. After the February quake, EQC was 'back to square one' on its inspections, having to reassess properties it had looked at after the September event. Teams of inspectors started a city-wide rapid-assessment process, classifying every property as having a low, medium or high level of damage.

When assessments proper started, claims of missed damage, improbably low valuations of what was identified, and combative or unreliable assessors

dogged the process. Even before the February quake, EQC had either sacked, or not renewed the contracts of, about 50 loss adjusters, mainly because they were unable to handle the workload or did not interact well with claimants.

After the February quake, there was no honeymoon period. First came the contractors doing emergency repairs on houses, who complained of months-long delays as they waited for payment after invoicing EQC for the work they had done. The delays had started after the September quake, but got worse after February and led to contractors asking homeowners for cash upfront or taking out loans. EQC maintained that all invoices, correctly submitted, were paid within about three weeks.

Part of the wider problem was the scale of the job, but this wasn't all of the earthquakes' making. As many quake authorities were fond of repeating, the February disaster was unprecedented in the magnitude of the shaking and the size of the insurance event. Presented with such an enormous task already, it is perhaps surprising that EQC assumed a much broader role than the one laid out for it.

The Earthquake Commission Act 1993 makes no mention of a managed repair scheme, but in October 2010 EQC took on Fletcher Construction to oversee the repairs for claims valued at between $10,000 and $100,000.

This continued after February, and the logistics of the job — inspecting properties, referring them on, giving quotes, accrediting contractors, doing the work, referring customers on again if they wanted someone else to do the work, approving any changes, signing off on the work and paying everyone who needed to be paid — proved, and continues to prove, rather challenging.

Most of the above was bypassed if the homeowner wanted to 'opt out' of the Fletcher repair scheme and employ their own outside contractor, but this managed to create controversy too. In July 2012, EQC changed the rules for leaving the scheme. Previously it would approve quotes, inspect completed work and pay contractors directly, but the new system left homeowners responsible for the bills.

Critics labelled the move anti-competitive, saying homeowners couldn't be expected to be project managers, much less ones who carried the financial can if contractors had to be paid before EQC could reimburse them. It was a move to keep EQC's own project manager, Fletcher, sweet, they claimed, by keeping as many repair jobs as possible in-house. One opt-out contractor appealed, unsuccessfully, to the Commerce Commission.

EQC's reasoning for the move was to make the whole process easier, but by late 2012 it had had no marked effect on opt-out rates. The total number of people leaving the scheme dropped over some months, but not by enough to establish a trend.

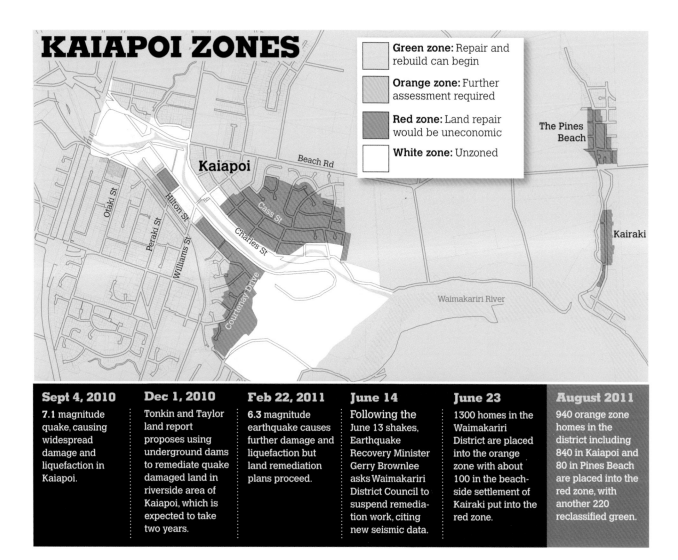

# KAIAPOI ZONES

**Green zone:** Repair and rebuild can begin

**Orange zone:** Further assessment required

**Red zone:** Land repair would be uneconomic

**White zone:** Unzoned

Kaiapoi

Beach Rd

Otaki St

Peraki St

Hilton St

Williams St

Cass St

Charles St

Courtenay Drive

The Pines Beach

Kairaki

Waimakariri River

| **Sept 4, 2010** | **Dec 1, 2010** | **Feb 22, 2011** | **June 14** | **June 23** | **August 2011** |
|---|---|---|---|---|---|
| **7.1** magnitude quake, causing widespread damage and liquefaction in Kaiapoi. | Tonkin and Taylor land report proposes using underground dams to remediate quake damaged land in riverside area of Kaiapoi, which is expected to take two years. | **6.3** magnitude earthquake causes further damage and liquefaction but land remediation plans proceed. | Following the June 13 shakes, Earthquake Recovery Minister Gerry Brownlee asks Waimakariri District Council to suspend remediation work, citing new seismic data. | 1300 homes in the Waimakariri District are placed into the orange zone with about 100 in the beach-side settlement of Kairaki put into the red zone. | 940 orange zone homes in the district including 840 in Kaiapoi and 80 in Pines Beach are placed into the red zone, with another 220 reclassified green. |

Christchurch became a city of many colours after the earthquakes. In August 2011, 840 orange-zoned homes in Kaiapoi and 80 at Pines Beach were red zoned and 220 were reclassified as green.

The EQC Act also has no reference to geotechnical drilling programmes, but the commission assumed this responsibility too. The government's zoning programme for residential land in greater Christchurch grouped properties in two zones: green and red. Within the green zones are three 'technical categories'. If your house is in the third of these — TC3 — it means your land is considered the most badly damaged in the category that is still economically repairable.

Again, things got complicated. The zoning programme was a broad-brush exercise. If you were zoned TC3 it meant the government *thought* your property was damaged. It was its best guess, based on the land information it had. To be sure, and to know what kind of repairs you would need, much more specific data was required.

Geotechnical drilling was needed on most, but not all, TC3 properties, to find this out. There are about 28,000 of these properties, spread among

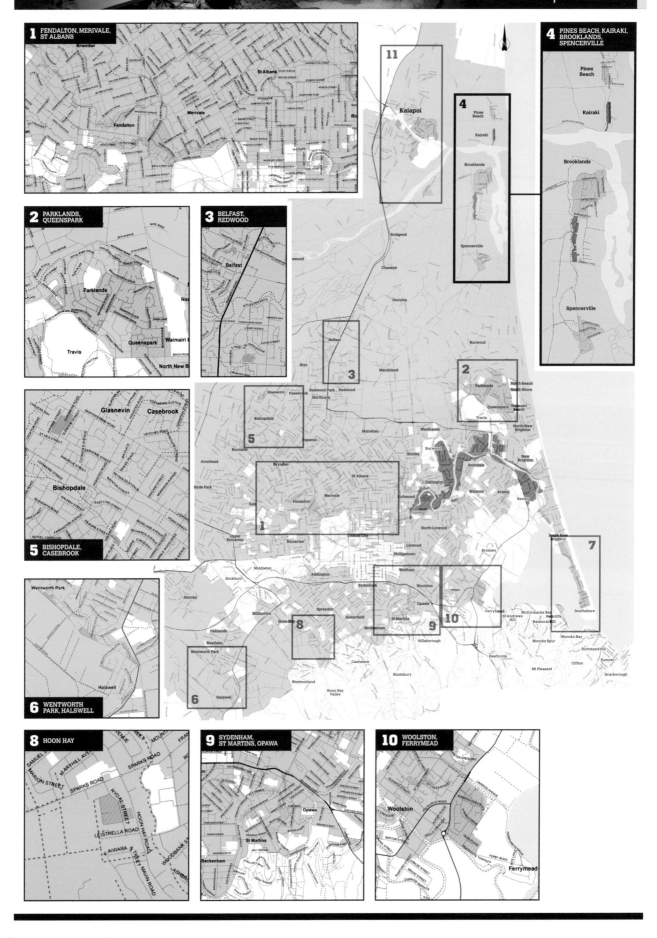

**1** FENDALTON, MERIVALE, ST ALBANS

**2** PARKLANDS, QUEENSPARK

**3** BELFAST, REDWOOD

**4** PINES BEACH, KAIRAKI, BROOKLANDS, SPENCERVILLE

**5** BISHOPDALE, CASEBROOK

**6** WENTWORTH PARK, HALSWELL

**7**

**8** HOON HAY

**9** SYDENHAM, ST MARTINS, OPAWA

**10** WOOLSTON, FERRYMEAD

**11**

many different insurance companies, which will be paying for their repairs or rebuilds. There is also EQC. TC3 properties with less than $100,000 of damage are its responsibility.

So, EQC started drilling on the properties it was responsible for in April 2012. Others followed suit, and soon there was talk of a joint drilling programme to avoid costly duplication and create comprehensive area-wide land data.

Then there was more talk. And more. Everyone involved could see the merit in pooling resources, but no one could agree how to do it. Finally, in September 2012, they agreed to disagree, and instead stressed the advantages of 'parallel' drilling.

A database of land information now exists, but there is an unspoken understanding that insurers will have to contribute some information to be able to make use of it. EQC expects to finish drilling early in 2013, possibly ahead of schedule. Private insurers expect to be done by 2014.

The commission was entitled to take on these two huge projects — the managed repairs scheme and geotechnical drilling — despite the law it was established under not spelling them out. However, the legislative shortcomings were not news to the government. In a 2008 briefing to incoming EQC Minister Bill English, the commission said it did not have the 'mandate or capability' to provide the response and recovery support expected after a big natural disaster.

Income from its earthquake levy did not cover its increasing exposure to soaring property values, it said, as the estimated value of land covered by the commission had more than tripled from $65.6 billion in 2003 to $207.6 billion in 2007. At the same time, the commission's income from quake levies rose just 9.25 per cent. The commission recommended increasing its cap for covering building damage from $100,000 to $200,000, and raising the levy to protect against growing financial exposure.

None of its recommendations were adopted by the government at the time, but the EQC levy has since been tripled to replenish funds. The Earthquake Commission Act 1993 is currently under review, and a performance review of EQC's response to the Canterbury earthquakes is expected to follow.

**JUST A MONTH** after the February quake it emerged that EQC and insurers disagreed on who was liable for what over multiple earthquakes. There had been three major quakes by then, and several minor ones big enough to generate fresh insurance claims — something the Earthquake Commission Act 1993 didn't provide for.

There were a couple of loopholes here that could see EQC pay claimants more than once:

- If it had been able to assess a property damaged in the September 2010 quake and make a full payout ($100,000 + GST) before the February 2011 one, it was liable for the same amount if the property was damaged again.
- Equally, if insurance cover rolled over between September and February, the EQC cover was reset.

Homeowners outside these groups — read 'most people' — were only eligible for one $100,000 payout from the commission.

Insurance companies, baulking at the idea of picking up the tab for all remaining damage over multiple quakes, sought the help of the High Court. Three judges ruled in their favour, and 'apportionment' was born. Simply put, this meant that every time there was an earthquake that prompted insurance claims, EQC was liable for the first $100,000 of damage.

This created a problem. The ruling came in September 2011, after many sizeable quakes had come and gone, leaving EQC to sift through all the properties with multiple claims and decide which damage was caused by which quake. Homeowners who had received one $100,000 payout and thought their insurance company would take care of the rest faced going back one step in the process.

Cumulative damage that had previously put them over the EQC cap could conceivably be spread across several events, leaving them under the threshold, despite having well in excess of $100,000 of property damage.

*The Press* documented several such cases, where distraught homeowners thought they were in their insurers' hands and on their way to a sizeable repair or rebuild. EQC, sensibly and to its credit, said it would not seek to recover one-off over-cap payments that had been paid 'in good faith'.

The EQC–insurer solution was to jointly assess the affected properties and decide if those who now found themselves with possibly hundreds of thousands of dollars in damage, but still 'under cap', ought to be in the hands of their insurer. In January 2012, EQC identified about 700 properties that fell into a limbo category, either through apportionment or 'significant differences' in the public and private insurers' assessment of damage.

Apportionment was a good example of the complexities the insurance industry faced, although cynics would argue it was another case of providers evading responsibility wherever possible.

The myriad problems, loopholes, delays and frustrations are too great to document fully. About the only thing most people can agree on is that, like EQC, the private insurance industry was not ready to cope with such a phenomenal event.

In an average year, New Zealand insurers collect about $3 billion in premiums and pay out almost as much in claims. As mentioned earlier, the Christchurch earthquakes are expected to cost them about $20 billion. Given those circumstances, the system has worked remarkably well for most people, but it has failed an unfortunate minority. Complaints have two common themes: 'my claim is taking too long to settle' and 'my insurer is trying to short-change me'.

There were the big differences over repair bills with EQC assessors, long negotiations with the Canterbury Earthquake Recovery Authority (CERA) on the future of commercial buildings, and a government minister who sometimes took exception to what he saw as the industry's self-interest.

'The Government has stepped up . . . EQC has stepped up . . . and CERA has stepped up,' Canterbury Earthquake Recovery Minister Gerry Brownlee said in July 2012. 'Now the private sector needs to do the sort of things that the private sector claims it can do so particularly well. I've lost my patience.'

Among the problems the minister was referring to was the huge workload that saw claims progress at glacial speed, and the reluctance of insurers to approve repairs until the earthquake risk dropped dramatically. The Insurance and Savings Ombudsman's Office set up a team to deal with Christchurch complaints after receiving about 250 queries.

As early as March 2011, big insurers announced they were no longer offering new cover in Canterbury. If you had a house policy you could

**LEFT** The February 22, 2011 quake destroyed this house on Bealey Ave.
**MARTIN DE RUYTER**

**MIDDLE** The EQC got mobile in 2011. Canterbury events manager Reid Stiven shows off the commission's campervan, which visited residents affected by quake damage.
**KIRK HARGREAVES**

**RIGHT** After the deadly February quake, the EQC's rapid assessment team visited Christchurch's River Rd, badly affected by liquefaction and lateral spreading.
**JOHN BISSET**

probably transfer it to another property, or buy a house and take the policy that came with it, but a fresh policy was out of the question.

Brownlee went to Monte Carlo in September 2011 to try to persuade international reinsurers and underwriters to re-enter the market here, but returned empty-handed. By late 2012, providers were slowly warming to the idea of writing new policies again. A CERA report from October 2012 listed most of the major insurers as offering new cover in TC1 and TC2 areas, and continuing to offer cover to existing clients in TC3. None, though, were writing new business in TC3.

**THE ZONES THEMSELVES** have become second nature to Christchurch residents. 'I'm green-blue,' one homeowner could say to another, and both would know that meant the property was in TC3, with all the attendant issues around how it could be repaired or rebuilt. But the dialect was largely confined to the city limits.

Zone life became part of many Cantabrians' lives in June 2011. That was when the government first confirmed that thousands of properties in greater Christchurch had land damage too costly to fix, and the owners would receive payout offers. Essentially, they had to leave.

About 5100 properties were red-zoned in that announcement. Some land proved more complex to affix a zone to — another source of frustration for

homeowners — and was classified 'orange zone'
or 'white zone'. Over nearly 18 months from June
2011, CERA gradually rezoned properties from
orange and white to green. By late 2012 the red
zone numbered nearly 8000 properties.

Compensation offers were either a 2007 rating
valuation (RV) payout for an owner's land and
house, or a payout on the land only. The latter
option was for people whose houses were total
losses, as they could negotiate with their insurer
for an indemnity or full replacement settlement —
almost certainly of greater value than a 2007 RV.

The dual-RV payout option was for red-
zoners whose houses were not write-offs. This
group found itself in a tricky situation. The
residential red zone was, while necessary, an
artificial construct imposed by the government.
Private insurance companies were not bound by
it. It didn't matter to them that the land, and by
association the houses on it, had essentially been
condemned. If their client's property didn't need
rebuilding, they weren't going to pay them out as
if it did.

The government therefore offered a dual
payout for such people, and they had no real
choice but to take it, even though a 2007 RV was
probably less than pre-quake market value and
definitely less than the cost of building another
house.

The insurers' position here was
understandable. Why voluntarily pay out more
than you need to? But sound financial reasoning
means little to a homeowner faced with Hobson's

choice. A red-zoner who had, say, a mid-20th-century house in east Christchurch, perhaps near the banks of the Avon River, had little chance of finding something similar in the city. Many have picked up sections in one of the subdivisions that have sprung up in the north and west of Christchurch, and while these are perfectly nice properties, brand new and on more reliable ground, many of these people will tell you it is not what they had.

For many quake-hit residents, the recovery process was underscored by the belief that insurers weren't playing fair. Years of nauseating television commercials where providers assured customers they were 'there for them' suddenly rang hollow now that they needed support to replace what they had lost. The negative perception some insurance companies had already cultivated for themselves was further entrenched.

The rebuild versus repair debate was a constant talking point and often crept into the pages of *The Press*. With sometimes depressing frequency, residents who contacted the newspaper with their troubles only had them solved or at least expedited after calls by journalists to the provider in question.

The issue arose when residents were assured in the early inspection stages that their house was damaged beyond repair and, under the terms of

*For many quake-hit residents, the recovery process was underscored by the belief that insurers weren't playing fair.*

their insurance policy, would be replaced. Then there would come another inspection, in which it was resolved the house was repairable.

The change was particularly galling for residents who had been red-zoned before their insurer's change of tune, and were faced with the non-choice outlined above, and the knowledge that their insurer would never have to prove it could do the repairs it said it could on a red-zoned property. Cynics could be forgiven for seeing it as a cost-saving exercise.

With no EQC or land damage issues in the process, commercial insurance went more smoothly.

'There's no question EQC have played a bit part in complicating matters,' John Grant, at the time Lumley Insurance earthquake response manager, said of speedier commercial settlements. 'It's just the structure of the dual insurance system.'

However, even in December 2012 *The Press* reported delaying tactics by insurers to force weary claimants into accepting lowball settlement offers. Customers with full replacement policies were accepting indemnity payments — sometimes half the value of a property, or even less. One Christchurch property lawyer said insurers stood to save millions through the practice. At least one big central-city property owner said that after fighting with his insurer he settled for less than rebuild cost 'so I could move on'.

The commercial sector also suffered the bulk of the underinsurance woes. Kiwi expert Michael Drayton put the shortfall at 20 to 30 per cent in many cases, and said the issue frequently arose in disaster recoveries internationally. Inflation often meant the full replacement values that commercial buildings were insured for were outdated, he said, and infrequent valuations left owners exposed too.

The Christchurch City Council was one of the chief culprits. Its damaged underground infrastructure, including water and wastewater systems, was insured for nearly $200 million less than it needed to be when all claims were lodged. City councillor Tim Carter said the city's assets were 'grossly underinsured' and called, unsuccessfully, for a review. Council staff said the shortfall was due to the scale of the earthquakes, which had not been anticipated by its insurers.

The sector had its own casualties, too. Canterbury's biggest residential insurer, AMI, needed a government guarantee to cover its losses, and its remaining interests were later bought by IAG for $380 million. With government backing, AMI's 11,000 over-cap claims, worth about $1.8 billion, were taken over by a new entity — Southern Response. The claims management company is expected to operate for about five years.

Ansvar Insurance announced in November 2011 that it was withdrawing from the New Zealand market after being swamped with $700 million

in claims. Ansvar specialised in insuring heritage buildings, especially churches; it covered, among others, the Anglicans' ChristChurch Cathedral, the Catholics' Cathedral of the Blessed Sacrament, and the Arts Centre.

A vote on a contingency plan for insolvency in June 2012 brought customers uneasily close to the reality of reduced payouts, but the provider always maintained it was on course to fully honour all its claims. By December that looked more likely: Ansvar had settled 19 of its 25 largest claims in Canterbury, which amounted to 76 per cent of its total claims, and had paid nearly $400 million in full and final settlements.

Western Pacific Insurance, which failed in 2011 leaving about 7000 policy-holders out of pocket, had its policy book labelled 'absurd' by its receivers. The company had only $32.7 million available to satisfy $41.2 million across more than 150 quake claims. Its lack of reinsurance was made worse by its habit of aggressively chasing a market share. By the time it failed it had written more than $7.8 billion of cover.

Uninsured residents, especially in the red zone, remained the only unknown. The government announced compensation offers for those without cover in September 2010, and included others who had fallen through the compensation cracks to date — owners of vacant and

**TOP** AMI customers visited an information tent set up by the insurance company on Stanmore Rd to help deal with the volume of quake claims being received.
**KIRK HARGREAVES**

**BOTTOM** Residents of the technical category 3 zone protest about their treatment by the Earthquake Commission and IAG. WeCan! organiser Mike Coleman talked to the protesters.
**DAVID HALLETT**

commercially zoned land in the residential red zone. All were offered half the most recent RV of their land, and commercial operators could get the full value of any buildings on their property.

The offer drew outrage from some of those affected. Residential red-zone compensation offers were linked to property owners' house insurance policies, and commercial and vacant landowners argued they had been unfairly punished. Since vacant land cannot be insured and commercial operators had, understandably, insured their assets through commercial policies, neither qualified.

Gerry Brownlee offered a contradictory response to their plight. While acknowledging that neither group could have done any more to insure themselves, he said it would be unfair for the government to offer them more. 'We think this is as good as we can do in the circumstances while at the same time keeping faith with the people who have covered themselves,' he told *The Press*.

Uninsured residents argued a different line. Many had consciously decided not to insure, but saw no reason why a red-zone offer had to be inextricably linked to a person's private insurance status.

In late 2012 all three groups were considering legal action. Red-zoners unhappy with the limited options offered by the Crown pursued independent legal action as well.

One of these was former children's television presenter Olly Ohlson, who in January 2013 appealed for donations to fund a $30,000 High Court challenge to save his red-zoned Brooklands home. Upset that he would never recoup the value of the condemned (but repairable) house, Ohlson planned to contest the Crown offers on the grounds that as he would have to rebuild elsewhere, he should be entitled to full replacement compensation. Negotiating with his insurer would only give him the repair cost — far less than an indemnity or full replacement value — leaving him no option but to accept a 2007 RV payout for his house and land.

Ohlson is not alone in his unrest. Fifty-three earthquake-related legal cases were filed in the High Court in 2012, with the rate of application increasing. Lawyers have warned that the trend is only the 'tip of the iceberg', and costly battles could overload the court system for years.

**FOR ALL THE** upheaval the earthquakes wrought, when it comes to insurance people will notice the cost and availability of ongoing cover the most.

By early March 2011, talk in *The Press* had turned to insurance and the implications for the industry. Comparisons were drawn with other quake-prone regions like California and Japan, where earthquake cover is

The sign on a red-zoned home says it all.

**KIRK HARGREAVES**

prohibitively expensive, amid the possibility that it might never be offered in Canterbury again.

However, quake-related insurance is slowly becoming more available in affected areas, but at a cost. Insurers have to obtain reinsurance from understandably cautious providers overseas, and meet some costs, such as excesses, themselves.

Tower Insurance announced in October 2012 that its home and contents premiums would rise about 30 per cent nationally and by more than 50 per cent in parts of Christchurch. About the same time, IAG, Vero and Lumley all relaxed restrictions on insuring new residential customers, and now consider them on a case-by-case basis. New-house cover had been hard to get and a handful of people had found themselves in the absurd situation of owning a new home — having obtained builders' risk insurance before the quakes — they could not move into. Builders' risk insurance expired the second the keys were handed over, and the lack of house cover made moving in too big a gamble.

On the commercial side, NZI, a subsidiary of IAG, has started offering contract works insurance for new commercial and big residential projects.

In 2013 most major insurers will switch to 'sum insured' policies for house cover. Vero and IAG will follow AA Insurance in covering clients for a total sum, specified by the homeowner, as the replacement cost of a property. The change shifts the onus for rebuilding onto homeowners, who will have to have an understanding of rebuild costs when they take out a policy and each time they renew it.

This is a protection measure for insurers. Insuring houses for a finite dollar amount gives their reinsurers a clearer view of their natural disaster risk and keeps house insurance in the post-quake New Zealand market affordable. Both Vero and IAG expect to have completed the switch by June 2014.

*Too many people have been let down by their insurers over these earthquakes. Many have got or will get what they are entitled to, but there is a minority who deserve better.*

Few Cantabrians would argue that their earthquake insurance experience has been easy or straightforward. On this front more than any other, Prime Minister John Key must surely regret his June 2011 statement that no one in Canterbury would be worse off because of the quakes.

Plainly, some people are. Not necessarily because their insurers did a poor job, but because the nature of the disaster meant some people could not get back everything they had lost. They endured huge waiting times for settlements, arguments over the cause and extent of damage and, slowly, the realisation that some of what they had had was gone forever.

Equally, some people are doing well. If your badly damaged house was in dire need of a lick of paint and some new carpet anyway, earthquake repairs could give you exactly that — for free.

If nothing else, the quakes have highlighted that insurance, public and private, is a commercial enterprise. Those in the game are there to make money, like any business, and duly act that way, but there is an uneasy sub-context to their behaviour. Too many people have been let down by their insurers over these earthquakes. Many have got or will get what they are entitled to, but there is a minority who deserve better.

Insurers claim that they are fulfilling their legal requirements to their policy-holders, and they are. Somewhere, though, lies a moral obligation that too often is not being met.

The year 2012 was one of transition; hopefully 2013 will be the first year of recovery. ∎

Plans to merge Central New Brighton School with South New Brighton School at the southern site continued despite this protest in October 2012 watched over by Central New Brighton principal Toni Burnside. Education Minister Hekia Parata's controversial proposals for Christchurch schools angered many parents and residents in the city.

IAIN MCGREGOR

# EDUCATION
## LOOKING TO THE FUTURE

*Tina Law*

Education in Christchurch changed forever on February 22, 2011, in about 20 seconds. But the fallout from the earthquakes will continue to be felt for years to come as schools are closed and merged, and new ones are built.

**MOST CANTERBURY CHILDREN** were tucked up safely in bed when the September 4, 2010 quake struck in the early hours of the morning. But at 12.51pm on February 22, thousands of children were at school. Some were on a lunch break and others were in classes. Some were in swimming pools and others were in the city visiting the art gallery.

In all cases teachers have been praised for their efforts to keep children safe and as calm as they could. Teachers lined the children up on school fields, encouraged them to sing songs, played games, and generally comforted them until their parents came to pick them up. It took some parents quite some time to arrive, but the teachers remained until every last child had gone home.

Eight-year-old Trent is one of many Canterbury children who told his story in the book *When My Home Shook*.

'I was on the monkey bars and then it happened. I fell off and got winded ... Then I ran like a turkey with no bones ... The teachers called out our names ... then four of my friends kept me company, they were quite nice to put their arms around me and my arms around them. Our teacher said "let's play paper, scissors, rock". We played and I won.'

Mt Pleasant School became a tent city in the week after the quake, with up to 300 nearby residents camping on the school's field.

Schools, early-childhood education centres and tertiary institutions across the city closed on February 22 and it was at least two weeks before the first schools reopened. For many it was a month before alternative school sites could be arranged.

The University of Canterbury reopened three weeks after the quake with a limited number of courses and it was five weeks before all classes resumed. A number of buildings were out of action so courses were delivered from a tent town of 14 marquees in the arts and law car parks. The university's athletics oval and the Dovedale campus were also filled with 104 temporary buildings for office and teaching space. They will remain in operation for years to come as the university repairs its buildings.

Christchurch Polytechnic Institute of Technology's (CPIT) Madras St campus was inside the cordon and could not be accessed until April 5, 2011, so the institute spread its courses across the city. From March 14 it ran courses at its Sullivan Ave campus, the Cashmere Club and Lincoln University.

Schools also got creative about making sure their pupils did not miss out on too much learning, and many resorted to the internet and email to provide pupils with work. Many parents fled the city with their children and enrolled them at schools where the ground was more stable. At the post-quake peak, 10,207 Christchurch pupils were enrolled at other schools across New Zealand and 688 pupils had gone overseas. Another 1000 pupils swapped schools within Christchurch. In the 18 months after the quake most of the pupils returned to the city, but in July 2012 there were still 4311 fewer pupils enrolled than in July 2010.

Immediately after the quake, school staff and the Ministry of Education went into overdrive, organising alternative homes for the damaged schools and transport to get pupils across town to their new temporary schools. Eleven schools had to find temporary locations, including six secondary schools that shared sites at other schools.

One board of trustees moved too slowly for Education Minister Anne Tolley's liking. She dismissed the entire Linwood College board and brought in a commissioner to replace board members. A commissioner remained in place until a new board was elected in June 2012, by which time Tolley had herself been replaced as minister by Hekia Parata.

Attending school on a split shift, with the home schools taking the morning shift and the visiting schools the afternoon shift, took its toll on pupils and teachers. Classes were condensed, there was no lunch break, and pupils attended school for about an hour less than normal. Pupils on the late shift did not finish until just before 6pm and arrived home well after dark during the winter months of 2011.

Schools progressively returned to their home locations throughout 2011 and 2012, and as 2013 began just five remained off their original sites. They included two secondary schools, Marian College and Unlimited Paenga Tawhiti. By September 2012, a total of 21 early-childhood education centres had been permanently closed and a further nine were operating from temporary premises pending decisions on buildings or sites.

The June 13, 2011 quakes caused more damage to schools. Redcliffs School was forced to leave its site as more rocks fell from the cliff above and put into question the safety of pupils and teachers. In the two months after those quakes, the school made three moves before settling at the van Asch Deaf Education Centre in Sumner, where it remains.

The June quakes also saw another wave of families leave the city. By that stage, rolls at 17 schools in the eastern suburbs had dropped by an average of 16 per cent since February 22. The reduced rolls in city schools put huge pressure on school finances. While the government continued to fund schools based on pre-quake pupil numbers until the end of 2011, this was not extended into 2012. Many schools then had to either make teachers redundant or not renew fixed-term contracts. Education Ministry figures show that in 2012 the equivalent of 167 full-time teachers, or 4.5 per cent of the Christchurch teaching workforce, lost their jobs.

Some schools, including Redcliffs, used their 'rainy day' funds to pay the salaries of teachers the ministry was no longer paying for, because they did not want to lose valuable staff. School-roll drops continue to affect teacher numbers, and provisional figures show funding for the equivalent of 62.6 full-time teaching jobs was cut over 85 schools at the beginning of 2013. One secondary school had a funding cut of 11.7 full-time-equivalent staff and five primary schools lost 0.1.

However, it is not all bad news, with 52 schools receiving a funding boost because their rolls have increased. In fact, rolls at some schools have been expanding rapidly. Waikuku School, which is expected to move in 2014 to a new site down the road at the Pegasus development, started 2012 with 130 pupils and expects to have between 275 and 350 by the end of 2013.

# MARIAN ON BARBADOES

JOSEPH JOHNSON

2011 deputy head girl Devon Cattell, left, 2012 head girl Tayla Sumner and 2012 deputy head girl Sam Jones.

Marian College was badly damaged in the February and June 2011 earthquakes. Students helped pack up for the move to the Catholic Cathedral College site at the end of the year, including

Most Christchurch schools displaced after the February 2011 earthquake have returned to their original sites, but a handful, including Marian College, are still trying to make the most of their temporary sites.

Marian College has been away from its historical home in North Parade for more than two years, but pupils and staff have found that a school's culture and identity lie in the people, not the buildings.

'We may not be at our original site but we're still Marian, we still have the same community spirit,' 2012 head girl Tayla Sumner says.

Spending most of 2011 attending school in the afternoon at St Bede's College, and then moving to its existing temporary home on the southern edge of the Catholic Cathedral College site at the beginning of 2012, has brought the pupils and staff even closer together, Tayla says.

The 400-pupil secondary school could be at the Barbadoes St site until the end of 2015. Engineers have said the land at North Parade needs time to settle down after continuing to move long after the February quake. Another geotechnical assessment of the land is due to be completed in August 2013.

Marian College is one of two Christchurch secondary schools still displaced from their original sites — the other is Unlimited Paenga Tawhiti, which has moved temporarily to Canterbury University before it finds a central-city site.

The Catholic Education Office spent $2.2 million getting the new Marian site ready for staff and pupils. Existing classrooms were strengthened and refurbished, and eight new classrooms were either delivered to the school or built there.

Principal Anna Heffernan says staff worked through their summer holidays to come up with plans on how to smooth the pupils' transition to the new site. They ended up having a week of activities to welcome pupils. The buildings have also been named after people who have had solid connections with the school over the years. 'It was really important we didn't feel just like we were camping here. It's our place, our space.'

Initially there was also a concern that people would think Cathedral College and Marian were merging, but the two state-integrated schools operate separately and have different entrances and lunch breaks.

The school's maximum roll is 430, and it has dropped to around 400, but Heffernan isn't sure if that is related to the school's new location. Some people might be put off by the extra distance the girls have to travel to get to school, she says.

Tayla says she enjoyed her last year at Marian at Barbadoes, and while it would have been better to be at North Parade, she and the other girls did not dwell on this and quickly moved on. 'There was no point in wishing we were at North Parade. We celebrated our identity.'

She was just happy that they had their own space and a normal school day, after spending most of 2011 being at school from 1pm to 5.35pm. 'We still had one period to go and the boarders [at St Bede's] would be eating dinner and we'd be off to accounting.'

Lyndon Thompson enjoys the sunshine while waiting for his physics class at Canterbury University's tent city.

**BARRY HARCOURT**

**SINCE 2011, CANTERBURY'S** tertiary education institutions have faced unprecedented challenges. They have been forced to think differently, work more collaboratively, and cut costs wherever they can, all the while trying to keep their reputations intact by continuing to provide a quality education for thousands of students.

The emphasis now is well and truly on the recovery, and the three main tertiary providers — Canterbury University, CPIT and Lincoln University — have put together strategies to rebuild not only buildings but also domestic and international student numbers.

Soon after the quakes the government guaranteed it would give Christchurch's tertiary education institutions fee subsidies during 2011 and 2012, based on pre-quake numbers, but many believed this was not enough and that the subsidies should have been extended until the end of 2013. Lincoln, which was not as hard hit as Canterbury University, did not require the help because it was able to meet its domestic student numbers. But, like the other two institutions, Lincoln's international student numbers took a hit and it has issues with some of its buildings.

All three institutions have put together comprehensive business cases for support and have asked the government for additional financial help. The government has agreed to support Canterbury University's science and engineering facilities; Lincoln's science facilities will also get a boost, and CPIT's trades training will be expanded to help train people for the rebuild.

However, Canterbury University, the worst affected of the three institutions, has asked for more help as it struggles with the full financial impact of the quakes. Full-time-equivalent domestic student numbers at Canterbury fell by about 1800 in 2012 and international students by 400, resulting in a $16 million drop in tuition fees.

The university is also facing increased insurance costs, and it has to find an estimated $150 million, over and above insurance payments, to repair its damaged buildings. It has already chewed through a vast chunk of its $100 million reserves, and vice-chancellor Rod Carr said in 2012 that it was haemorrhaging $100,000 each business day.

A 10-year financial forecast showed just how bad the university's balance sheet was. It was due to post a $38 million loss in 2012, and is projected to continue running deficits for the next four years. The forecast says the institution will reach a predicted surplus in 2017, but it will take until 2021 before the university achieves its pre-quake 3 per cent surplus.

A university-wide call went out to save money where and when possible. Carr said he needed to cut 150 staff during the next three years, and two voluntary redundancy rounds were held. The first, in October 2011, attracted 39 applications and 24 were accepted. The second round, in 2012, attracted 31 applications and 12 were accepted.

Course closures were also proposed, including theatre and film, cultural studies, American studies, and operations research. The rationale presented for the closures was vigorously challenged by staff and, following a three-hour debate, the University Council decided to retain theatre and film studies and cultural studies, but American studies and operations research were closed. The closures affected seven full-time-equivalent staff.

In September 2012 the university decided to stop offering its English language programme until the end of 2014. The bridging course for international students who did not meet the university's English requirements had suffered from a loss of students and was set to lose $291,000 in 2012 alone. Four full-time and three part-time staff were affected by the closure.

The university's college of arts was targeted because it had lost one in four students since 2010 — the largest drop in student numbers out of the university's five colleges. Students protested at the proposals to close arts courses, which they believed were diminishing the arts programme at Canterbury.

Carr's response was simple and clear. 'The college offered more than

One of the first buildings on Canterbury University's Ilam campus was also the first to be demolished following the quakes. The distinctive copper-topped engineering lecture theatre was pulled down in November 2011.
**DEAN KOZANIC**

200 courses to only 2500 full-time-equivalent students and the university cannot afford to offer them all. The government is not prepared to pay us to continue to do all the things we do now, no matter how worthy they are.'

The vice-chancellor also upset law students by launching a restructuring that would see the law school merged with the college of business and economics and the law library moved to a floor of the central library tower.

Along with the most obvious ways of saving money — cutting staff and courses — the university also started to think laterally about ways of making money. It launched an appeal among its alumni and raised more than $3 million. And it engaged a team of property and financial advisers to explore ways to secure more private-sector money.

Selling off campus assets was not an option because most of them had already been sold over the years, Carr said. Selling the land at the university was also out of the question, because the university has already built on almost all the green land, apart from the Ilam Fields. However, Carr saw forming more public-private partnerships, similar to the one with global student accommodation provider Campus Living Villages (CLV), as an option. CLV runs the university's student halls and has a 40-year lease on the buildings.

The university moved to reverse the decline in international students and increase revenue by signing an agreement with global education provider Navitas Ltd. Navitas will establish an affiliated college on the university's campus that will recruit and prepare international students for degree study at Canterbury. The plan is to open the college in 2013 with a pilot of about 60 international students, expanding that to 600 students within five years and eventually to 1000 students. The university hopes the deal will bring in an additional $65 million in revenue over 10 years.

Despite the course closures and drop in student numbers, Canterbury managed to maintain a relatively high ranking among the world's top universities. It sits at number 221 in the QS World University Rankings, which considers more than 2000 universities before ranking the top 400. The university's college of engineering is ranked 134th in the world and the college of science is among the top 200.

As well as dealing with the fallout from the quakes, the university is trying to capitalise on the opportunities they have provided. It has become an epicentre for earthquake research, with more than 170 projects under way. The research findings are expected to help people in New Zealand and around the world understand the impact quakes have, not only on buildings and land but also on people and animals.

Engineers and geologists from around the world have flocked to the university because of their interest in quake-related research. But the quake research projects cover not only geology and engineering, but also geography, social science, history, anthropology, computer science, tourism, music, psychology, theatre and film, Maori and indigenous health and development, media and communication, education, art history, economics, human–animal studies and linguistics.

CPIT is also capitalising on opportunities arising from the quakes. Its trades training numbers have already risen, and the government has promised to help the institution expand its offerings in this area even further.

CPIT's domestic student numbers recovered in 2012, and while international student numbers

**TOP** Cost-cutting measures at the cash-strapped University of Canterbury included the Law Library subsumed into the Central Library in the James Hight Tower.
KIRK HARGREAVES

**BOTTOM** Canterbury students congregate in inTENTcity 6.3 Cafe a month after the quake of the same magnitude shocked the city.
CARYS MONTEATH

were still a little down on pre-quake figures they exceeded expectations. International education providers in Christchurch are all working together to reverse the decline in student numbers.

**THE INTERNATIONAL STUDENT** sector took a hammering following the earthquakes, when thousands of students left the city and did not return. Before the quakes Christchurch was home to a healthy international student market worth up to $370 million each year to the local economy. It is not known what that figure has dropped to, but international student numbers have almost halved from 11,206 between January and August 2010 to 5937 during the same period in 2012.

Canterbury Development Corporation international education sector leader Emily Branthwaite says student numbers had been falling in Christchurch and across New Zealand since a peak in 2003, but ironically the city had just started to experience its first upturn since then when the quakes struck.

She says the continued decline during 2012 was expected, despite a tail-off in aftershocks. Many students who were partway through their studies when the quakes hit decided to stay on, but left once they completed their courses. New students had not arrived to fill those places at the same rates as in the past.

Private language schools have been the hardest hit, Branthwaite says. Before the quakes there were more than 20 operating in the city, and now there are about seven. Many of the schools were in low-cost commercial buildings in the central city and ended up in the red zone. Many stopped operating because they could not find alternative premises and student demand was low. Those that have managed to survive are the top-quality providers who have long-standing relationships with their agents, Branthwaite says.

The loss of income from the drop in international students has affected many parts of Christchurch's economy. Not only have schools and institutions lost millions of dollars in tuition-fee income, but families who hosted the students have also lost income. Transport is another area affected by the drop, because international students are frequent users of public transport. They also traditionally spend money on tourism, and their parents usually come to visit at least once during their stay here, which all helped to add to the tourism spend.

Given the value of the sector to Christchurch there is a big push to attract students back. Auckland is home to 61 per cent of the international students now studying in New Zealand, and Christchurch has the second biggest share with 9 per cent. Before the earthquakes Christchurch had a 17 per cent share. The Christchurch sector has a goal of returning to pre-quake international student levels by the end of 2015, Branthwaite says. 'We need to get back on track pretty quickly.'

In March 2012, Tertiary Education Minister Steven Joyce pledged $5 million to help Christchurch's international education sector recover over the next four years. An initial $1 million went toward funding the Christchurch Educated initiative, which was launched six months later, in September. The initiative's goal is to reverse the decline, and it is developing a number of schemes to help this happen.

Before the launch, a lot of analysis and thought went into how best to attract students to the city. Branthwaite says the quakes forced the sector to take a good look at what it could do better, because it was doing some things really badly. The sector now has far greater levels of cooperation, she says.

Secondary and primary schools had always been good at attracting Korean students to the city, but the majority would go to other countries, including Australia, for tertiary studies. 'These students very rarely stay on and complete their tertiary education here. It's been a failure of the sector and the way it operated in the past that these kids never even considered Christchurch as an option for tertiary.'

Helping to address that issue is a new Tertiary Pathway Guarantee programme, launched as part of Christchurch Educated. The programme will see international pupils who have studied at a Christchurch secondary school admitted to one of the city's tertiary providers. They will also be guaranteed accommodation.

There are also plans to create a central-city meeting place and launch a student card, which could be an alternative to the Metrocard, to pay for public transport. The government has also extended working rights for some international students, allowing students in Christchurch to work up to 20 hours a week. At least one English language provider is attributing an increase in numbers to the increase in working rights.

There are already anecdotal signs that student numbers are beginning to increase, with Branthwaite hearing word that some schools are turning away students because they are full. 'Some of the schools are seeing some great enrolments coming through again.'

The feedback from the market is also positive, she says. At one point Korea would not even talk to Christchurch education providers, but a mission to Korea at the end of 2012 proved positive. 'The earthquake risk thing is old news now,' Branthwaite says. People are wanting to know if there is enough accommodation available, and what is around for students to do in the evenings and on weekends.

CPIT set ambitious targets for international students and is exceeding them. In late 2012 it had 545.5 full-time-equivalent international students, up from a predicted 530. That equates to $10 million in revenue for the institute, chief executive Kay Giles says.

The government wants to double the economic return from international education from an estimated $2.3 billion in 2011 to $5 billion by 2025. With these initiatives in place, Christchurch hopes it can help provide a decent chunk of that return.

**TOP** In September 2011, Languages International became the first English-as-a-second-language school to move back to the central city since the February quake. Jaroslav Beno, from Slovakia, left, and Yuko Nakahara, from Japan, discuss a question posed by teacher Sally Browning.
**STACY SQUIRES**

**BOTTOM** Languages International students Joyce Chuang, left, and Natsuko Saito, during an October 2011 class. Chuang, from Taiwan, was enrolled at Languages International before the September 2010 quake and was determined to remain in Christchurch.
**STACY SQUIRES**

**ONCE THE REALITY** of the quakes hit and the extent of the damage to the city's education infrastructure became apparent, schools quickly realised changes would have to be made. The cost of the damage, estimated to be up to $750 million, was too great for the government to absorb without change, especially when some schools had classrooms full of empty desks.

As the months wore on, the uncertainty surrounding the future of schools heightened. But all the time, teachers continued to focus on making sure children's education was not affected any further by the quakes.

Principals became more anxious about the unknown. They just hoped the changes would not be forced on them from on high and would involve extensive community consultation before proposals were announced. It looked like this was happening when, in October 2011, the Education Ministry launched a consultation programme to seek feedback on the future of Canterbury's education sector.

In May 2012 the ministry launched a draft document, *Directions for Education Renewal in Greater Christchurch*. The document contained no details on specific schools but mooted 20 proposals, including the development of education campuses that could include early-childhood education, primary and secondary schools, and tertiary institutions on one site, along with social services. It also advocated schools sharing facilities such as workshops, gyms, swimming pools, auditoriums and libraries.

The document also estimated it could cost between $500 million and $750 million over 10 years to repair 207 of the 214 schools in the region. People were invited to put in submissions, and were told that from August that year decisions would be released on the shape of the network.

However, on September 13, principals' worst fears were realised when Education Minister Hekia Parata dropped a bombshell on the city, announcing the proposed closure of 13 schools and the merger of another 26.

Schools were caught off guard by an announcement that was nothing short of a PR disaster. Parata and the ministry were subsequently subjected to heavy criticism for the way they announced the decision. Principals and board chairs were given a colour-coded name tag before being herded into a meeting room at the Lincoln Events Centre and handed a folder. Principals wearing purple badges were clustered into the 'rejuvenate' category, which actually meant their schools were mooted to close, merge or relocate. Those with orange badges were in the 'consolidate' category, which could also see them close, merge or relocate. Principals of schools to remain open were given a green badge.

The ministry was accused by principals of using misleading language. They questioned how the ministry could 'rejuvenate' schools by closing them down.

The press release handed to the media talked about the government

Education Minister Hekia Parata talks with Ouruhia School principal Mark Ashmore-Smith and board of trustees chair Lyn Bates (obscured) during a visit in November 2012. The school will stay open but move to a new site after 2016.

**IAIN MCGREGOR**

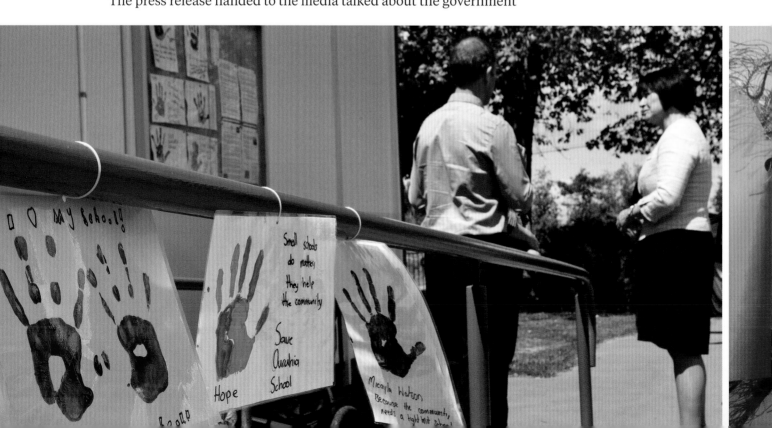

investing $1 billion over the next 10 years to restore the education sector. People had to read to the eleventh paragraph on the second page before finding out that the government was proposing widespread school closures and mergers.

Schools were also upset that they were provided with very little information about what to do next. It took another 15 days for Parata to announce a consultation period, in which schools were given 10 weeks to provide feedback and alternative options. Principals also accused the ministry of using incorrect information about schools to come up with the proposals.

During the consultation period, Parata spent almost three weeks visiting more than 30 schools that had been proposed for closure or merger. Given the level of outrage in the community the meetings were tense, with parents being warned beforehand to treat Parata with respect.

The proposals led to a number of protest marches through Christchurch and an 11,000-signature petition, calling on the government to halt the shake-up, was presented to Parliament.

Following an anxious wait, 31 schools were told their fates on February 18, 2013. Seven schools were proposed to close, 12 could merge into six and 12 would remain open. These were only interim decisions, so the schools unhappy with the proposals were given another chance to plead their case. Parata will deliver her final decision at the end of May 2013 but it will take years for some of the proposals to reach fruition and new schools to be built. Christchurch can now only hope it ends up with a state-of-the-art education system that will be the envy of the rest of the country and serve the city's children well for the next 50 years. ∎

# WHAT A MODERN SCHOOL LOOKS LIKE

Christchurch will be a city full of modern schools equipped to educate children for much of this century. That is the carrot being dangled in front of Christchurch residents to make the closure and merger of schools more palatable.

So what does a 21st-century school look like?

Classrooms are no longer positioned in rows. They are joined together in pods and open into communal areas.

Pupils sit on bean bags, work standing up at tall desks, or from a netbook on a couch.

Christchurch South Intermediate School is one city school that is already embracing a new way of educating children in modern classrooms. In the past two years, the school's wooden classrooms, built in 1939, have been replaced with 16 new classrooms at a cost of about $4 million. There are four classrooms in a block and they all open into a communal area via huge glass sliding doors, allowing pupils and teachers from different classes to work together. The doors can be shut, but teachers are encouraged to keep them open. The communal area has couches, bean bags, desks at different heights and other small, private rooms.

Having 120 kids working in the same area has the potential to create a noisy, disorganised shambles where very little learning gets done, but apparently the research shows this is how 21st-century kids learn the best and Christchurch South Intermediate School has proven it works in practice too.

The days of teachers standing at the front of the class for five hours have long gone. When *The Press* visited the school, the children had been given tasks to do and they were working independently in pairs. They didn't even raise an eyebrow when a reporter and photographer walked into the communal area. This usually stops a class and distracts them from their work.

A teacher-aide was working closely with a pupil who needed a little more help with his reading. Normally the child would have been isolated from the rest of his class, but the pair were working in the same area as the other children.

Technology plays a big part in the modern classroom, with most classes equipped with interactive whiteboards and netbooks. Christchurch South Intermediate principal Ross Hastings says some teachers were initially worried the open-plan style of the classrooms would distract pupils, but they have found pupils are more focused on their work.

Teachers now enjoy working in the new environment, and Tamara Blackwell says the open spaces allow her to work more closely with her teaching colleagues and they can feed ideas off each other.

Pupils also love the freedom to use different spaces, Blackwell says.

Pupils Kate Morley, 13, and Kayla Booth, 12, sitting on bean bags as they worked on a social studies project together, said they were happy not to be cooped up in the same room all day.

Christchurch South Intermediate School pupils enjoy working in one of their new teaching and learning areas, the Rutherford Pod. JOHN KIRK-ANDERSON

Christchurch South Intermediate School pupils Lily Williams and Josh Law, both 12, show homeroom teacher Tamara Blackwell their work.
**JOHN KIRK-ANDERSON**

# HEALTH
## GOOD PEOPLE DOING EXCELLENT THINGS

*Deidre Mussen*

Random strangers pluck up a little girl who is buried beneath her mother in rubble in the City Mall. She is carried to Christchurch Hospital's emergency department, where she becomes its first February 22 quake patient, arriving only a few minutes after the 6.3 killer devastates the city.

'SHE WAS LOOKING blue and awful,' emergency physician Professor Mike Ardagh recalls. The man who brought her in sits in the ambulance bay and sobs.

A steady stream of casualties follows. They include the little girl's crushed mother, who had been deemed dead by rescuers and covered by a sheet where she fell. Later, though, her protruding foot was spotted moving and she was taken to hospital three hours after her daughter. Miraculously, she survives.

'AFTER THE QUAKE, the injured, the desperately sad and the scared flooded into the hospital,' Professor Ardagh wrote in *The Press* in November 2012. 'They came on foot, on the backs of trucks, in strangers' arms, strapped to cars, carried on makeshift stretchers. They had to. The roads were a mess.'

In the first 24 hours after the quake, 6659 people were injured and 182 were killed. Seven of the deaths were recorded at Christchurch Hospital, though most of the seven were dead on admission. The final death toll reached 185.

The earthquake was deemed New Zealand's worst peacetime disaster, because of the number of fatalities and injuries, plus the large-scale destruction across Canterbury.

**LEFT** Survivors: Olivia Cruickshank and her daughter Abbie. They were both injured in Cashel St. Abbie was taken to hospital quickly but Olivia was left under a blanket, believed dead, for three hours.
**KIRK HARGREAVES**

**MIDDLE** Patients and staff gather outside the Emergency Department at Christchurch Hospital.
**CARYS MONTEATH**

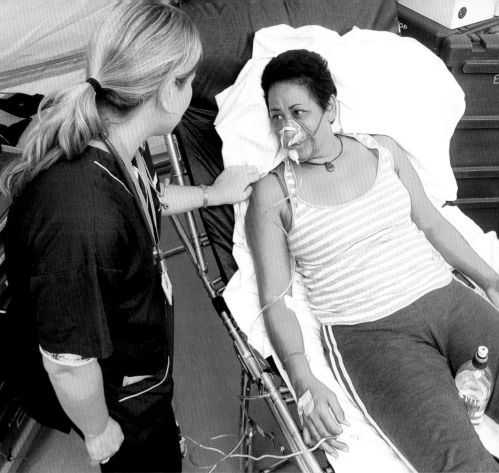

Nature's brutal force caused major damage at the public hospital, as it did to many of the city's health services. The hospital, home to the city's sole emergency department, kept functioning after the earthquake, literally just keeping its head above water.

'The lights went out, the phones didn't work, ceiling panels fell on people, bits of the hospital flooded, the elevators wouldn't take the injured upstairs to the operating theatre, the CT scanner or the intensive care unit, and the place kept shaking,' Ardagh recalls.

Broken pipes flooded the blood bank on the lower ground floor. 'It turns out they were ankle-deep in water with torches on their heads trying to match blood.'

Part of the ambulance bay collapsed, two floors of the hospital's Riverside block had to be evacuated, and both staff and medical equipment were tossed about like toys. The severe shaking immediately cut electricity but the hospital's six diesel generators activated seconds later to power essential services. Unfortunately, the violent quake and powerful aftershocks stirred up sludge in the diesel tanks, clogging the system and several times causing a generator to fail. That left vital parts of the hospital without power at times, including the emergency department, intensive care unit (ICU), blood bank and radiology department, until electricity was reconnected about four or five hours later.

The disaster's unprecedented scale, combined with damaged streets, traffic jams and communication problems, overwhelmed Christchurch's ambulance service, St John. Others stepped into the breach. A June 2012 review of the civil defence emergency management response stated, 'In the chaos of the city after the earthquake, the work of St John was complemented by that of many citizens, health workers and other emergency services who provided immediate first aid and transported injured to hospital or medical centres.'

Among those who provided on-the-spot first aid were four urology surgeons, in Christchurch for a conference when the quake struck, who crawled into collapsed buildings to help the injured. Australian urologist Lydia Johns Putra was one of these. Using a Leatherman multi-tool knife and a tradesman's hacksaw, she amputated trapped Christchurch man Brian Coker's legs under flashlight in the Pyne Gould Corporation building. She was helped by Christchurch Hospital anaesthetist Dr Bryce Curran. Brisbane urologist Stuart Philip helped many people at the PGC building, including Coker, who he resuscitated on the way to hospital.

Fellow urologist Stephen Mark, of Christchurch, helped survivors in the Arts Centre and ChristChurch Cathedral before heading to the collapsed roof of The Press building, where he and English urologist Julian Shah rescued and cared for trapped staff.

All four were later awarded the Christchurch Medal for their bravery.

In a further complication that day, quake damage to air conditioning forced St John to evacuate its inner city communication centre a few hours after the first shake. Dispatching and communications were channelled via Auckland, assisted by Police and Fire Service 111 communication centres, while St John kept operating from tents on its Durham St site.

As a result of the disruption to communication services, which included an overloaded telephone system, the hospital's emergency department received scant information about the scale of the disaster and the likely number of casualties. That lack of information further distressed staff, patients and relatives who feared for loved ones.

Despite these difficulties, the hospital was well prepared for a large-scale disaster, partly thanks to having had a trial run with the September 2010 quake and a feared bird flu epidemic. Staff swiftly swung into action.

Professor Ardagh's main recollection that dire day was 'good people doing excellent things under very, very unusual circumstances'.

After the quake hit, the hospital's mass casualty incident plan was activated, as it had been for the September quake, which saw 97 injured people seek its care, including three with serious injuries, but no deaths. Around 370 people arrived at its emergency department within three hours of the February 22 quake.

There was little triage for the injured who arrived at the hospital early on, but an outdoor ambulance bay was later set up for triage and to care for those with minor injuries who were too terrified to enter the hospital buildings. An emergency triage centre was later established in Latimer Square.

The influx was a test for a department that was used to an average of 220 patients a day. But the South Island's largest tertiary, teaching and research hospital, with a maximum capacity of 600–650 beds, was, in the words of the civil defence review, 'never really overwhelmed by the amount of trauma presenting'.

Fast juggling was needed to manage admissions of badly injured quake victims. Only four of the hospital's 18 ICU beds were empty when the quake hit, and it forced an urgent reshuffle of patients to free up beds for critically injured people. Within two hours of the quake, a national ICU teleconference was held to coordinate patient transfers out of Christchurch. In the first 24 hours, 14 patients were moved to other cities and 18 quake victims were admitted to the hospital's ICU.

A further 171 people were admitted to Christchurch Hospital on day one, many of them badly injured as a result of falls or being struck by falling

*Professor Ardagh's main recollection that dire day was 'good people doing excellent things under very, very unusual circumstances'.*

**TOP** Christchurch hospital anaesthetist Bryce Curran, who helped with an emergency amputation in the rubble, receives a Christchurch Earthquake Award from Christchurch Mayor Bob Parker.
**KIRK HARGREAVES**

**BOTTOM** Patients outside Christchurch Hospital after part of the complex had to be evacuated in the continuing aftershocks.
**CARYS MONTEATH**

rubble. Orthopaedics was the busiest service with 107 quake admissions, including 38 with crush injuries. Three people had both legs amputated, and two people each lost one leg. Of the 258 theatre cases and 914 surgical procedures, 55 per cent were orthopaedic.

Most casualties arrived at the emergency department in the first few hours after the quake, but some people who had been trapped and had to be extricated came later in a gravely ill condition. In total, 31 frail elderly broke their hips that day. Some took to their beds rather than travelling to hospital and turned up in subsequent days. Outpatient clinics and elective surgery were cancelled for several weeks to free up resources.

**IMPORTANT LIFESAVERS THAT** day were the care provided by Christchurch Hospital and its location, nestled on the western side of the city's badly damaged central business district.

'The massive peak ground accelerations, the time of the day, and the collapse of major buildings contributed to injuries, but the proximity of the hospital to the central business district, which was the most affected, and the provision of good medical care based on careful preparation helped reduce mortality and the burden of injury,' the civil defence review stated.

'Hospital facilities were remarkably resilient but some, such as the main hospital, only just held together. The top two floors of the [Riverside] ward block were evacuated because lifts were not working and access to the adjacent building did not exist at these levels,' the review continued.

The hospital was helped by triage at sites where many people were injured and the primary health sector diverting less critical cases to several other non-acute hospitals in the city, including Southern Cross Hospital and Princess Margaret Hospital. Southern Cross, a private hospital, worked with an adjacent major primary healthcare service, Pegasus Health 24-hour Surgery, to manage its quake patients.

While most of the worst injuries occurred in the inner city, out in the suburbs impassable roads forced thousands of battered residents to go to other primary healthcare services.

Staff from hospitals around New Zealand poured into Christchurch to help out, equalling 3058 person-days of support from other district health boards. Other assistance came from overseas, including an Australian field hospital, which set up for several weeks at Cowles Stadium in Aranui to help care for the injured and act as a community health site.

'The main hospital was very fragile, especially since its operating theatres could have become unusable if the tunnel conveying services had collapsed. This use of the Australian field hospital was prudent,' the civil defence review stated.

The review lauded the health sector for how it coped with the quake, commenting: 'The health response was very good, largely because of the high level of preparedness in the Canterbury District Health Board, Pegasus Primary Health Organisation and the Ministry of Health locally.'

It praised the district health board's 'strong leadership', noting that its management was used to dealing with emergencies. Emergency department staff and clinical leaders had practised dealing with sudden large influxes of serious trauma in exercises, ensuring it was well prepared.

Research by Professor Ardagh and colleagues from Otago University's Christchurch medical school and the Canterbury District Health Board was

Patients are treated in the Australian field hospital, which served as a treatment centre and community aid service for several weeks.
**KATE GERAGHTY**

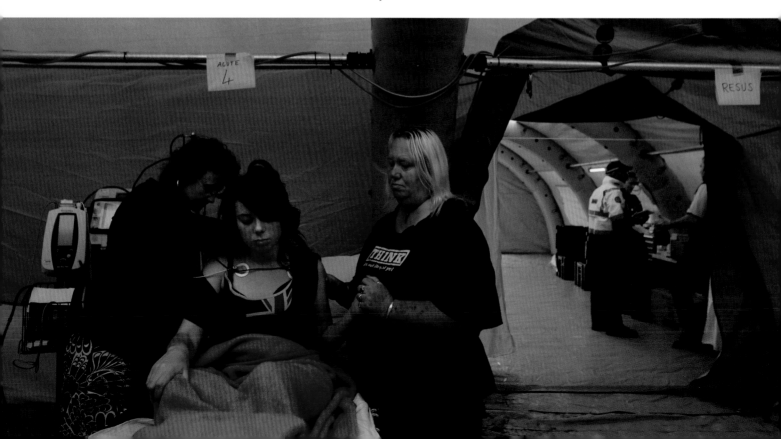

published in *The Lancet* medical journal in April 2012 and supported the conclusion that the hospital had performed well during the quake.

The researchers' views were echoed from an unexpected quarter. Ironically, the then-president of the Royal College of Surgeons of Edinburgh, Dr David Tolley, was also in Christchurch for the urology conference. His wife Judy suffered a nasty scalp laceration in the February 22 quake so the couple ended up at the hospital's emergency department.

Dr Tolley later praised the hospital for its efforts in an article in the College's newsletter, writing: 'The outstanding care which I saw delivered in the emergency department that day did not simply happen by chance. It is a standard which has been achieved as a result of training across many different disciplines and when it mattered most, it stood up to the most robust challenge imaginable.'

**THE QUAKES HAVE** left a legacy of shattered lives and health services. Their horrific toll is spelled out in the statistics of the Accident Compensation Corporation (ACC), New Zealand's no-fault compensation scheme for all personal injuries to residents and visitors.

But ACC's figures also highlight the level of effort dedicated to helping affected people rebuild their lives. By mid-January 2013, ACC had accepted 13,201 claims for the three major earthquakes, subsequent aftershocks, rescue and clean-up activities plus injuries from quake-damaged property and items. By then it had paid out $24.4 million in compensation, treatment

The Dental Service brought in two mobile units to keep operating after the quake.

**DEAN KOZANIC**

and rehabilitation, mainly for soft-tissue injuries, lacerations or puncture wounds, fractures or dislocations, and dental injuries. Public health acute-service costs were excluded.

February's quake was the most expensive disaster in ACC's 39-year history and resulted in the most claims, costing $19.2 million for 6365 claims by January 2013. In 2012, ACC chief executive Ralph Stewart estimated that care for people injured in the quakes would cost about $200 million in the long term.

Most of those who suffered significant injuries were expected to be rehabilitated and to return to independence. Of 558 people awarded weekly compensation for quake injuries, only 37 were still receiving payments by mid-January 2013. However, ACC was supporting eight people who were unlikely ever to regain full independence as a result of injuries received in the February quake. These included moderate to severe brain trauma, spinal cord injuries, multiple amputations and major burns.

Death-benefit grants of almost $1.9 million, including funeral grants of more than $890,000, were paid out for 185 claims. Most were from the February quake, but two claims were from the September 4 quake. Weekly death-benefit compensation was also paid to 60 people, at a cost of almost $4.8 million.

ACC had accepted 12,193 claims for medical treatment, 288 claims for hospital treatment, 364 claims for dental care and 72 work-related mental injury claims. Ten people received lump sum payouts, totalling $527,800; one was from the September 4 quake and the rest from the February quake.

The impact of the quakes on the mental health of Canterbury residents has been high, with thousands of aftershocks keeping stress levels up. University of Canterbury researchers Amy Rowlands and Charlotte Renouf found levels of acute stress, anxiety and depression were higher for those living in hard-hit areas. Those levels dropped in the months following the February 22 quake but remained high during 2011.

A 2012 Canterbury Earthquake Recovery Authority (CERA) wellbeing survey found 66 per cent of 2381 Canterbury residents polled had suffered distress or anxiety associated with ongoing aftershocks during the year. More than half believed their quality of life had deteriorated.

A raft of organisations offered post-quake support and counselling, including Red Cross, the government's earthquake helpline and Lifeline. Lesser-known organisations worked hard behind the scenes to help struggling residents. One out-of-town example is Skylight, a Wellington-based social enterprise that supports those facing tough times through change, loss, trauma and grief, providing training and supporting those assisting them.

**TOP** Robbie Drew from the Red Cross delivers care parcels.
**KIRK HARGREAVES**

**BOTTOM** Carol Gallagher and Coleen Falvey bring Red Cross supplies to a Civil Defence welfare centre.
**JOHN BISSETT**

Within a week of the February quake, Skylight had produced an employer handbook called *When Trauma and Grief Come to Work*, handing out 10,000 copies to Christchurch workplaces in a bid to support the grief-torn city. Four months later, the organisation was awarded a special commendation from the annual New Zealand Workplace Health and Safety Awards for producing and distributing the booklet.

'It is fantastic to have our work recognised, but given that it was for such a tragic and massive event as the Christchurch earthquakes, it was a privilege to be able to help,' Skylight's chief executive, Bice Awan, said at the time.

Southern Regional Health School's (a state school for children from Year 1–13 who are too sick to attend their usual schools) Christchurch school had a surge of children suffering stress-related problems after the quakes, upping its roll by 60 per cent by the first month of 2013.

Research has also found that smoking rates and alcohol consumption have increased, likely a coping mechanism in response to the ongoing stress.

The Asthma Foundation funded a study on the impact of the quakes on smoking levels, polling 1001 Christchurch residents. It found more than 10 per cent of non-smokers had smoked at least one cigarette since the September 2010 quake, and 34 per cent of smokers had increased their tobacco consumption. Smoking rates increased around the time of the September and February quakes.

Researcher Nick Erskine concluded that it appeared the earthquakes had increased the city's smoking rates, with people lighting up to help them cope with stress, but called for more research on the subject.

Temporary, cramped housing was also having an impact on the community's health. The incidence of influenza was quadruple the national

average during the 2012 winter. At the time, Christchurch Hospital virologist Lance Jennings told *The Press* Canterbury's influenza rate was 226 per 100,000 people, while the national average was 52 per 100,000.

'The winter has been particularly severe. It's been cold — much colder than last winter — and people in Christchurch are living and working in cramped conditions post-earthquake,' he said.

Quake damage to the environment also had the potential to affect the health of Christchurch residents — things such as liquefaction, broken sewerage pipes, groundwater contamination and deteriorating air quality as a result of higher levels of dust and more people using fires for heating.

The largest earthquakes all caused liquefaction, including those of September 4, 2010, February 22, 2011 and June 13, 2011. The Institute of Environmental Science and Research (ESR) studied health impacts from liquefaction and groundwater contamination, and in a June 2012 report noted that health risks from liquefaction were low unless it had been contaminated by sewage. It also noted that most residential sites tested for *E. coli* showed liquefaction was not contaminated with sewage.

However, the report said that in areas where sewage had contaminated liquefaction, pathogenic viruses and protozoa could persist for more than five months after the contamination, regardless of its depth. It recommended people should avoid contact with sewage-contaminated liquefaction, avoid touching their mouths if handling it, and wash their hands thoroughly with soap before preparing food.

ESR also studied health impacts from liquefaction dust. Its June 2012 report noted that the potential impacts of airborne dust included

A runner exposed to liquefaction particles, seen as grey patches on the ground and dust in the air. Sludge which came up through liquefaction of the ground during three of the quakes was found to be of low health risk unless it was contaminated. Authorities recommended people should avoid contact with it if they thought it contained sewage.

**DEAN KOZANIC**

Mike Ardagh, professor of emergency medicine at the Christchurch School of Medicine and Health Sciences, recalled the influx of the injured into Christchurch Hospital: 'They came on foot, on the backs of trucks, in strangers' arms, strapped to cars, carried on makeshift stretchers,' he said.

**CHRIS HILLOCK**

respiratory or eye irritation as well as more serious effects from inhaling particles smaller than 10 micrometres (PM10), which could penetrate lungs and potentially cause premature death. Work by ESR and Environment Canterbury found that PM10 increased markedly after big earthquakes.

The closest air-monitoring station to the central business district was in St Albans. 'It is reasonable to assume that exposures in the worst-affected suburbs were significantly higher than indicated by the St Albans data because more liquefaction occurred in these areas,' the report noted.

One of the huge success stories of the February earthquake was the lack of a gastroenteritis outbreak despite massive disruption to the city's water and sewage systems, thousands of people being forced to remove liquefaction in residential areas, plus people having to move into crowded accommodation and welfare centres.

The Canterbury District Health Board's public health arm, Community and Public Health, was responsible for the public health emergency response. Quake damage forced immediate evacuation of its Chester St East headquarters and it initially set up at Christchurch Women's Hospital, but within three days of the quake it moved into the Christchurch Art Gallery.

The unit pumped out messages to the community, including welfare centres, providing advice on hand washing, good sanitation, boiling water, food safety, infection control and isolation of infectious people.

'The public health response was amazing,' Professor Ardagh says. 'We were planning for half the city getting gastroenteritis.'

Portaloos had popped up around many suburbs, and competitions were held to see who could build the best garden latrine while the city's sewage system was carefully repaired. Public health staff also embarked on widespread water testing and started chlorinating water within a week.

A report into the quake's public health response, published in March 2011, noted concerns about 'the risk of gastroenteritis outbreaks in a situation of contaminated water and disrupted sanitation'. Testing picked up 155 instances of contaminated water around the city in the first month after the quake, but swift action to flush the system and chlorinate water stamped out any problems.

People on home dialysis were evacuated from Christchurch because of their need for clean water.

**IT IS A** long road back, as health services work to repair and replace damaged facilities. As the Canterbury District Health Board's 2011/12 annual report stated in late 2012: 'We still have a fragile system beset with uncertainties.

'The earthquakes dealt the Canterbury health system a huge blow

in terms of losing people, buildings and infrastructure, and based on international evidence, we are yet to see the full human impact of the quakes on our community.

'With a perfect storm of stressors, it's remarkable that the Canterbury health system hasn't imploded. Somehow our people have continued to meet the ongoing challenges of ever-changing health needs of our population.'

Canterbury District Health Board chair Bruce Matheson and chief executive David Meates noted that the first two years post-quake were 'just the beginning of the challenges'.

'The repairs and rebuilds taking place are very disruptive for staff and patients. Despite the less-than-ideal working conditions with ongoing building repairs and constant quake-related disruptions on the home front for the 16,500 people who work in health in Canterbury, the DHB has continued to achieve outstanding results and deliver world-class services. This is a credit to the professionalism and patient-focus of those working in our health system.'

As for damage to buildings, the Canterbury District Health Board, the region's largest health provider, estimated repairs would cost about $160 million. Most of its 200 buildings were damaged, 9000 rooms needed to be repaired, and 106 hospital beds were lost.

In February 2013, Meates said 30 of its buildings had been closed because of damage, 21 were quake-prone but still in use, and 30 had major structural weaknesses. Damage to two medical wards in Christchurch Hospital's Riverside block forced general medical services to shift to the board's Princess Margaret Hospital in Cashmere. Medical services are expected to remain split between the two hospitals until mid-2013, when a multi-million-dollar acute medical assessment unit is due for completion at Christchurch Hospital.

Work designed to boost the hospital's surgical capacity had also started, with new wards being built to replace those lost in the quakes. Office space was converted at other hospitals to create 73 replacement beds for the 106 lost, but that meant patients needed to be transferred between hospitals around the city. And it left Christchurch Hospital with fewer beds than pre-quake. The dental and acute stroke units, some laboratory services and community mental health services also had to shift.

Aside from the necessary repairs, the earthquakes have led the Canterbury District Health Board to fast-track plans to upgrade Christchurch and Burwood hospitals. In 2009, the health board had proposed a $400 million upgrade of Christchurch Hospital, including dedicated cancer and children's facilities plus more operating theatres. The proposal was submitted to the Ministry of Health in 2010. The broader plan, along with redevelopment of Burwood Hospital, was mooted to cost $1 billion.

The earthquakes put those plans on hold, but in September 2012 Earthquake Recovery Minister Gerry Brownlee announced government approval for the revised redevelopment project. This is expected to be the largest single investment in public health facilities in New Zealand, with a cost of around $600 million. Work at Burwood will start first, and is due to be completed by late 2015. Christchurch Hospital's redevelopment is earmarked to finish by mid- to late 2018.

Meanwhile, private hospitals continue to help prop up the public health service, boosting their theatre space to ensure residents continue to get the care they need.

Christchurch Women's Hospital, the only South Island building with a base isolator designed to protect it from powerful earthquakes, also required about $4 million in quake repairs. While the 10-storey building performed well, it suffered some cracks and cosmetic damage on each floor.

Elsewhere in the community, health services are slowly recovering from the quake damage. After the February 22 quake, 19 community pharmacies and five general practices either closed or were badly damaged, 635 rest-home beds were lost and many dental and mental health services were lost or displaced.

Of 160 non-government organisations (NGOs) in the city, 94 kept fully functioning but the rest had to close, move to new premises or offer limited services. Community mental health services were hit particularly hard, with 26 mental health organisations losing their buildings in the quake.

Securities House, a seven-storey building in Gloucester St, was demolished in March 2011. It housed a range of district health board and NGO mental health services, including the Anxiety Disorder Unit, Bipolar Support Canterbury, Anxiety Support Canterbury, Kakakura Health Service, Psychiatric Consumers Trust, Mental Health Education and Resource Centre, Obsessive Compulsive Disorder Support Group, Mental Health Foundation of New Zealand and Social Phobia Support Group.

Three organisations — Bipolar Support Canterbury, Anxiety Support Canterbury and Psychiatric Consumers Trust — have since merged and become the Mental Health Advocacy and Peer Support Trust, moving into new premises in Spreydon.

Community House in Hereford St, which was home to 23 community services, also had to be demolished because of quake damage. That left health services based there homeless and scrambling for new facilities, including Heart Children New Zealand Inc.'s Canterbury branch, Mensline, Disabled Persons Assembly, Nga Maia Maori Midwives and Natural Fertility NZ.

While Canterbury's health services and residents have borne the brunt of the earthquakes, there have also been significant impacts further afield. Seismic assessments of health facilities around the country have identified many earthquake-prone buildings. Grey Base Hospital, in Greymouth, is one such, facing major repairs because of its vulnerability to quakes.

WHILE BUILDINGS AND lives are rebuilt around Canterbury, a swarm of research into the impacts of the earthquakes will continue for many years.

Researching the Health Implications of Seismic Events, or Rhise, has been set up to look at the health repercussions of the quakes. The group's members include representatives from the Canterbury District Health

A Metro bus passes along Oxford Tce in front of Christchurch Hospital and the Otago Medical School building housed in the city. Canterbury District Health Board estimated repairs to its structures would cost about $160 million, and about 9000 rooms in 200 buildings would need to be repaired.

DAVID HALLETT

Board, universities and polytechnics, St John, Pegasus Health and other primary health organisations. Professor Ardagh, who is New Zealand's only professor of emergency medicine, is the chair of Rhise. He says the research will provide insights that will be of interest internationally, and will be important in planning future disaster responses.

The group's establishment was partly prompted by overseas universities contacting New Zealand's health services, eager to research the quake's health impacts. 'We were keen to own it and also keen to share it,' Professor Ardagh says.

In September 2011, the Health Research Council of New Zealand and the Canterbury Medical Research Foundation announced they would jointly fund five research projects into the health implications of all the major quakes. This includes a project by Ardagh to create a Canterbury-wide de-identified database of those people who were injured and unwell in the first three days following the February 22 quake.

This is a world first, providing an overview of a complete healthcare response to a major earthquake where the entire response was from local providers who were also affected by the disaster. The database will be available for other researchers around New Zealand to use for their earthquake studies, 'so they don't have to dredge it up themselves'.

Professor Ardagh says one unusual feature of Christchurch's earthquakes was that the city relied on its sole acute hospital with an emergency department to care for seriously injured people, which made it vulnerable. Fortunately, the hospital was able to continue functioning.

'There was no question we were lucky in many respects. The hospital was knocked about but it didn't fall over.

'One hospital might fall over. It was a compromised system responding to its own disaster.'

Ardagh says similar-scale disasters in recent times have either occurred in third world countries with woefully inadequate health services or in first world countries, such as Japan, with a huge population and wide pool of health resources that could take over if hospitals in affected areas were unable to function.

Other research by Christchurch Hospital includes a study into staff stories of their experiences of the February 22 earthquake at work, which was due for publication in a nursing journal in early 2013. 'Some of the things that people did are amazing,' Professor Ardagh says.

Canterbury University's GeoHealth laboratory is testing whether there is a relationship between the extent of physical damage from the earthquakes on neighbourhoods and non-injury health outcomes, such as liquefaction increasing levels of heart disease.

Otago University researchers will consider occupational health impacts of the earthquakes on front-line workers, such as police, fire fighters and ambulance staff. University researchers will also study stress cardiomyopathy, commonly called broken heart syndrome, brought on from the extreme stress of the earthquakes. 'We know that after the earthquakes, we had a lot more heart attacks,' Ardagh says. Another area of research is why two-thirds of those injured and killed in the quakes were female.

Crush injury syndrome, and particularly surgical practices around such injuries, is another area of study. Professor Ardagh says that in the aftermath of the February quake surgeons struggled to find suitable best-practice for such injuries because much of the research had been done in third world countries where healthcare was gravely delayed, altering outcomes.

*From the start, there has been a steely determination to rebuild the city's crumbled foundations and lives.*

**TOP** Local artwork adorns a new outpatients building at Christchurch Hospital as a tradesman makes finishing touches to a doorway.
**IAIN MCGREGOR**

**BOTTOM** Christchurch Hospital from the air. The modern Christchurch Women's Hospital, the white building in the foreground, stood up well to the earthquake but other parts of the complex suffered significant damage.
**DAVID HALLETT**

**CLEARLY, CHRISTCHURCH'S EARTHQUAKES** have had a dramatic impact on the region's health services and the health of its residents. Health services face years of disruption as the rebuild continues and residents battle the ongoing impacts of this terrible disaster.

But redeveloped health services will be just one of many positive legacies. Lessons learned in the aftermath of the quakes are likely to help not just Canterbury but the whole of New Zealand become a healthier place.

From the start, there has been a steely determination to rebuild the city's crumbled foundations and lives. This is nowhere truer than in its health services. As Christchurch mayor Bob Parker said within days of the February 22 quake: 'There will be a new and stronger city rising out of the ruins.' ∎

More than 100,000 road cones have adorned the highways and byways of Christchurch since the first earthquake struck on September 4, 2010. On February 22, 2012, the first anniversary of the city's deadly quake, people around Canterbury and the world filled the tops of cones with flowers to remember that tragic day.

**JOSEPH JOHNSON**

# INFRASTRUCTURE
## PUTTING THE CITY BACK TOGETHER

*Sam Sachdeva*

Some of the worst destruction in Christchurch's February 2011 earthquake occurred out of sight. Below the ground, raw sewage from broken mains leaked into the city's shattered water pipes, while thick power cables were stretched by up to a metre, cutting power to most of the city.

**THE SHEER SCALE** of damage to the city's infrastructure, and the immense repair programme put in place to fix it, has also stayed beneath the surface as a tale that has largely failed to capture the public's imagination. In a way that is understandable — water, power and other essential services are largely taken for granted by most people on a daily basis. But as the thousands of residents who were forced to use chemical toilets and boil their drinking water for months can attest, the loss of those services was far from trivial.

The February shake broadened and widened the damage caused by the September 2010 quake, which had been most merciless in the city's eastern suburbs. Christchurch City Council water and waste manager Mark Christison, fleeing the council's central city offices on February 22 with other shaken staff, quickly realised the scale of the devastation.

'When I came out on the street, I knew we were in trouble because the land was liquefying there and it hadn't on September 4, so we knew it was going to be a lot worse.'

City Care chief executive Onno Mulder, leading one of the city's main infrastructure providers, was also under no illusions about the magnitude of the work facing the city.

'I dusted myself off, got my family safe, and said to my wife that I was going to work because I was going to be busy. That was probably the understatement of the century.'

**LEFT** Twisted and broken power cables lie in pools of liquefied sand and silt as Prime Minister John Key visits Orion New Zealand workers trying to reconnect the power to the Bexley Ave substation on March 3, 2011.
**FIONA GOODALL**

**MIDDLE** Major damage to the Bromley sewage treatment plant in the February quake led to fears the oxidation ponds might turn anaerobic and send clouds of foul gases across the city.
**CARYS MONTEATH**

The two men are part of a cast of thousands taking part in a daunting five-year, multi-billion-dollar repair programme to return the city's infrastructure to, and in many cases improve on, its pre-quake state. It is a task that few would envy, yet one that has been accepted with enthusiasm and dedication. Already, there have been some surprising signs of progress in a city that, post-quake, has often felt mired in endless delays.

**RAW NUMBERS PAINT** a picture of the damage caused to Christchurch's water and sewerage network. The earthquakes damaged around 528 kilometres of the city's sewer system — more than 30 per cent of the entire network — and 51 kilometres of water supply mains. All but 64 of the city's 175 freshwater wells need some form of repairs, while 100 sewer pumping stations have to be rebuilt or replaced.

Critical facilities such as the Huntsbury water reservoir and Bromley wastewater treatment plant were badly damaged, forcing officials to quickly develop repair and rebuild plans to ensure residents had access to key services.

Mulder says the unobtrusive nature of the city's infrastructure has made it difficult for contractors to understand the true extent of the damage. 'It's all underground, it's all buried so you can't see it. It's not like a building where you can visually inspect the damage then move on — we've had to check it all.'

Contractors have had to go through a methodical process to inspect the pipes. First, jetting trucks blast silt loose with high-pressure hoses before it is gulped up by the sucker trucks that have become a constant presence on the city's streets. Only then is it possible for workers to get any idea of what repairs are necessary.

To speed up the inspection process, officials have turned to the latest technology. Christchurch is currently home to more than half of the country's underground closed-circuit television capacity, with 20 buggy-mounted cameras making their way through hundreds of kilometres of pipes to check for damage. Officials are also using measurements from manholes to build a digital three-dimensional model of the wastewater network, giving them a rough idea of which pipes have shifted the most. What they have seen is a medley of pipes made from different materials and using different techniques, reflecting the city's history.

Some have fared worse than others — earthenware pipes shattered in the ground, while the high-density polyethylene pipes installed following the September 2010 quake came through the February 2011 shake and subsequent aftershocks unscathed.

Starting with the big pipes and working their way down, Mulder said workers have had to painstakingly repair numerous breaks along a single pipe. 'The pipe is broken, and two metres down it's broken again, then there's [a break] at another two metres, and another two metres, so you're constantly trying to trace it down.'

The breaks to the sewer network meant some residents had to endure months without working toilets. Portable toilets, better known as portaloos, were a common sight on city streets following the February 2011 earthquake, with *The Press* reporting nearly 3000 in use at their peak. The portaloos, and the household chemical toilets distributed by officials, are now almost extinct, with sewer services being restored to all city streets in August 2011.

The extent of the damage to the sewer system, and the possibility that it could have contaminated the city's drinking water, forced officials to chlorinate the water supply immediately following the February 2011 quake — a big decision given Cantabrians' historic pride in their untreated water. But, as Christison noted, the potential health problems could not be ignored. Officials felt vindicated by the lack of any major outbreaks of water-borne disease by the time chlorine was removed from the supply in December 2011.

The city's waterways were also a victim of the damaged sewer network. The Avon and Heathcote rivers, the city's estuary and Scarborough beach were all declared off-limits for more than a year following the September

TOP A sign warns of polluted water in the Avon–Heathcote Estuary while Christchurch City Council workers undertake land surveying. Christchurch's beaches were technically closed and off-limits for several months after the February quake because of pollution from broken stormwater and sewerage pipes.
**DAVID HALLETT**

MIDDLE LEFT City Care worker Greg Mitchell about to send a motorised CCTV camera underground to check drains.
**DON SCOTT**

MIDDLE BOTTOM Several thousand portaloos sprang up around mostly eastern parts of the city. Breaks in the sewer network meant some residents had to endure months without a working toilet inside their homes.
**DEAN KOZANIC**

RIGHT City Care workers dig up and begin to repair broken water pipes on Matipo St, Riccarton, after a large aftershock very close to the city on the morning of October 19, 2010.
**DEAN KOZANIC**

2010 quake, as officials were forced to discharge raw sewage and wastewater into the waterways to ease strain on the damaged network. When they were declared open for use in November 2011, *The Press* reported that about 7.8 billion litres of untreated wastewater — enough to fill 3100 Olympic-sized swimming pools — had made its way into the city's rivers.

Christison was aware of the problems caused by the discharge but said it had been an unfortunate necessity. 'Our priority was to keep sewage out of people's backyards and off the streets.'

The city's power network, managed by lines company Orion New Zealand, also took a battering. Orion was once envied by many in the New Zealand power industry for running the country's most trustworthy network, with the least power outages, for many years. But the February 22 quake turned the company's grid on its head: in a matter of seconds, the network suffered more faults than would normally be seen in a decade.

Power was cut to three-quarters of the city, with four large underground cables supplying power to the east damaged beyond repair and a New Brighton substation sinking two metres into the ground. *The Press* reported that Orion's lines-repair subsidiary Connetics, which would do about 50 repairs to its 11,000-volt underground cables in a normal year, fixed about 1400 faults to 250 cables in the 12 months after February 22. That damage, combined with a 10 per cent drop in demand for power, has seen Orion's revenues take a $30 million hit.

A $155 million upgrade over the next 10 years will cover repairs to nearly every major part of the network, while also expanding the company's reach to the new subdivisions that are popping up to accommodate quake-

displaced Cantabrians. However, the massive upgrade will hit residents' pockets, with householders set to pay an average of an extra $1000 each in increased power bills over the repair period.

While the cost is not to be sniffed at, it could have been far worse: Orion chief executive Rob Jamieson estimated that a seismic strengthening programme carried out in the years before the quake had saved about $65 million in potential repair costs.

**MEANWHILE, A HOME** had to be found for the millions of tonnes of silt sucked from the city's sewers and streets, along with earthquake rubble from the remnants of demolished buildings. In March 2011, the Christchurch City Council agreed to set up a massive rubbish and recycling park in part of Bottle Lake Forest. The site, which had been temporarily commandeered by Civil Defence immediately following the quake, is expected to process about 4.25 million tonnes of rubble from central-city buildings, residential homes, roads and pipes, as well as 380,000 tonnes of silt.

The Burwood Resource Recovery Park, as it is known, has not been without controversy: nearby residents expressed concerns about the noise and dust from dump trucks frequenting the site, while a public outcry forced the council to back down on plans to dump thousands of tonnes of material containing asbestos there.

Despite the problems, the work will continue for some time: in September 2012 a resource consent was granted to allow earthquake rubble to be dumped at the park until 2017.

**AMID THE CHAOS** of the earthquake, even Christchurch's dead could not avoid feeling the impact of the magnitude 6.3 shake. Thousands of gravestones across the city took a battering, with some toppling over and others teetering precariously. Memorials crumbled and obelisks snapped in half, while rows of urns at one crematorium miraculously escaped damage after the memorial wall holding them disintegrated.

Teams of workers have been ensuring that the larger headstones are put in a safe place to avoid any danger to visitors, while also developing a plan for repairs and calculating the likely cost. The team managing the repairs says the process could take a decade, with over 7000 headstones to inspect and repair.

The city's historic gravestones, some of which date back 150 years, have been given priority by the Christchurch City Council. However, the cost of repairing non-heritage headstones will lie with families, leading to fears that the city's cemeteries will never be the same.

**PLANES, BOATS AND** cars were also affected by major damage to the city's transport networks. The city's port, a vital South Island freight link, was hammered by both major quakes. Two of Lyttelton Port's 1400-tonne cranes were jolted off the ground and out of their rails on February 22, while there was significant damage to wharves, piles and the reclaimed land on which much of the port sits.

The scale of the damage has forced the port to divert most of its cruise ships to Akaroa for the foreseeable future, with the small Banks Peninsula town now receiving up to 200,000 visitors each season.

The port company's 1959 office building has also been demolished after an engineering assessment found it was too damaged for an economically viable repair. The company has been reluctant to release any figures that would reveal the cost of repairs, but the bill for insurers is believed to run to about $500 million — putting it on track to be the biggest single corporate insurance claim ever made in the southern hemisphere. An ongoing wrangle between the port and its insurers over tens of millions of dollars of payouts has complicated the process.

Despite these obstacles, the port is still running successfully: record volumes of containers and coal were behind a strong result in its most recent financial report, with freight levels expected to increase as the rebuild gathers pace. The port is also putting the rubble from Christchurch's demolished buildings to good use, using it as part of a reclamation project to add as much as 10 hectares to its working area.

Christchurch International Airport, the main point of entry to the South

Island for many tourists, escaped significant physical damage but could not avoid the impact of the devastating images being broadcast from the city to potential visitors. The number of passengers going through the airport annually has dropped by more than 450,000 since 2010, and some airlines have temporarily cut the number of flights going through Christchurch until demand recovers.

Despite this, airport bosses aren't worried. Their research shows that overseas airports that have had to deal with a major disaster have seen their numbers return to normal within about two years. The airport has also received a shot in the arm from the government, which has announced a new 'open skies' policy, making it easier for foreign airlines to set up new Christchurch routes.

Christchurch's roading network has also taken a battering, with undulating roads a daily reality for residents. About half of the city's 2000-kilometre road network was damaged by the quake. According to *The Press*, the Christchurch City Council has recorded more than 50,000 defects on road surfaces. That damage, coupled with the devastation in the city's eastern suburbs, has put extra strain on the city's roads. Traffic jams are now the norm on previously free-flowing roads in western Christchurch, while public buses have been forced to reroute around the central city cordon, extending the length of trips for many commuters and causing passenger numbers to drop.

**LEFT** The Lyttelton Port Company is using hard fill from buildings demolished after the quakes to extend its land out into the harbour.
**CARYS MONTEATH**

**MIDDLE** The land reclamation is taking place along the harbour edge by the port company's coal-handling area.
**DEAN KOZANIC**

**RIGHT** Traffic jams and road chaos have become a way of life for Christchurch residents since the earthquakes began in September 2010. Here traffic piles up on the Main North Rd near St Bede's College on a wet autumnal day in 2011.
**DON SCOTT**

While a temporary bus exchange set up in the central city provided a stopgap solution, public transport provider Environment Canterbury (ECan) quickly developed a range of changes to plan for the future of post-quake public transport. These changes, unveiled in November 2012, saw fewer routes going directly into the central city and more heading to suburban 'hubs' and outlying parts of Canterbury. The government's own transport plan, released in November 2012, based its bus network around ECan's proposal.

The government plan also included a proposal to slow traffic to 30 km/h in the heart of the city, with improved routes for cyclists and pedestrians. However, it omitted one of the most discussed, and most controversial, transport options brought up following the earthquake — a light rail network. The council's central city plan included a $406 million light-rail connection between the central city and Canterbury University as the first stage of a citywide network. However, the proposal, promoted enthusiastically by Christchurch mayor Bob Parker, was put aside by Canterbury Earthquake Recovery Minister Gerry Brownlee.

The dream is not over, however. The council's draft transport plan, setting out how Christchurch's transport network would develop over the next 30 years, included a possible investigation into heavy and light rail.

# CONE SWEET CONE

In the wake of the Christchurch earthquakes, a wide array of no-frills objects used in the rebuild have taken on a life of their own. The shipping container has won praise for its ability to house any number of different businesses, while the portaloos that once lined some streets were often resplendent with decorations. However, it is difficult to top the versatility, popularity and ubiquity of the humble orange traffic cone. Look around nearly any street in Christchurch and you will see at least one cone silently standing guard.

Traffic companies told *The Press* there were about 100,000 road cones strung out on the city's streets, with a value of more than $3 million. To residents, the cones' value is more symbolic. They have transformed the objects into an art medium, giving them an opportunity to express themselves and bring a sense of humour to some of the city's most damaged areas.

The cones were bedecked with tinsel on Christmas Day and bounding with bunnies over Easter, while thousands were filled with flowers to mark the first anniversary of the February 22 quake. The 'flower power' celebrations struck a chord around the world, with people in Australia, London, Singapore and Mexico among those who decorated cones as a tribute to the bravery and stoicism of Cantabrians.

Christchurch artist Henry Sunderland, whose cone-themed cartoon was the prime inspiration for the decorative work, was overwhelmed by the response to what was a simple attempt to make people smile. 'It is about having a wee idea and allowing people to express it in a personal way. People in Christchurch need that,' he told *The Press* at the time.

That sense of fun was evident in an exhibition from polytechnic design students in November 2011, with a cake, an upturned icecream and a gramophone horn among a range of reinterpretations.

Some have even managed to combine the practical with the ceremonial. After tying the knot in May 2012, Gillian and Doug Mackinnon walked into the wedding reception at their family's badly damaged Kaiapoi home through an avenue of road cones.

The life of a $31 cone is not always so easy. Many have been run over, thrown into rivers or lobbed on top of buildings, while the objects are also popular acquisitions for students. The cones cannot be vanquished quite so easily, however. With the infrastructure rebuild programme getting into full swing, earthquake-related roadworks — and the orange icons — will be a common sight for years to come.

Road cones are now constant companions on the roads of Christchurch.

**TOP LEFT** A Christmas-themed cone on Withells Rd.
**DON SCOTT**

**TOP MIDDLE, TOP RIGHT AND MIDDLE** Flowers adorned the tops of road cones on the first anniversary of the February 22, 2011 quake to commemorate those lost.
**JOSEPH JOHNSON**

**BOTTOM** Another season amid the road cones. Spencer Hayes, 11, left, and his brothers Foster, 2, and Kaspar, 7, got into the Easter spirit by decorating cones and the western wall of their house.
**DON SCOTT**

**AS INFRASTRUCTURE REPAIRS** have slipped under the radar, so too have the efforts of the team working behind the scenes to put everything back in place. Thousands of workers flooded in from across the city, all over the country and around the world to help put the city back together.

Australian workers mingled with Aucklanders following a major aftershock in June 2011, while companies that had traditionally fought each other for business shared beers and laughs at a number of barbecues to keep morale up.

City Care, which had 500 staff when the September 2010 quake hit, boosted its numbers to 1300 to deal with the aftermath of the February 2011 quake. Mulder said the company's Pages Rd offices were transformed into an operations centre, where council experts joined City Care workers to plan temporary repairs and a long-term fix.

'We brought the field staff, they brought the engineers, and that's where we ran the recovery from: all the decisions were made there.'

Staff out in the field faced what could only be described as inhospitable conditions. Some worked with water and sewage up to their knees as aftershocks rattled the earth around them, while power repairmen worked into the night to fix wires ripped from people's homes following significant shakes.

On top of the physical toll, Mulder said workers also had to deal with being separated from their loved ones at a time when Cantabrians just wanted to stick together. 'Most people could go home and be with family and friends, but we had to be out there and working, and that's taken a toll.'

Despite the gruelling nature of their work, Mulder said his staff and all the other workers he met were unflinchingly committed to getting the city's services back in action as soon as possible. 'They didn't want to have time off — they wanted to work, they wanted to be out there, and they wanted to be part of it.

'They felt like they were part of something bigger than them.'

Their work has not gone entirely unrewarded: workers spoke fondly to *The Press* of receiving home baking, hot mugs of tea and warm embraces from residents who were fully aware of just how important their work was.

Those individual workers are small but significant cogs in the larger machine powering the infrastructure rebuild — one that was set in motion as the dust was still settling in the city. Within 48 hours of the February 22 quake, Christison was relieved of his Civil Defence duties to start developing long-term repair plans for the city's essential services.

Less than three months after the earthquake, the government unveiled a public-private hybrid of official agencies and contractors to work as a team on the $2 billion rebuild. The Canterbury Earthquake Recovery Authority, the city council and the New Zealand Transport Agency have combined

**TOP** Mount Pleasant School pupils, including Meera Patel, 12, took home baking to the Traffic Management workers in charge of road cone positioning and traffic flow. Grant McNicholl can't believe his luck.
**KIRK HARGREAVES**

**MIDDLE** Rob Skurr from Ching Contracting in Nelson works to restore the water supply to Sumner and Redcliffs residents after the magnitude 6.3 February 22 earthquake.
**DAVID HALLETT**

**BOTTOM** Mark Ford, head of infrastructure for the Stronger Christchurch Infrastructure Rebuild Team (known as Scirt), announces plans for a new sewage pump plant in Bromley.
**CARYS MONTEATH**

with five private contractors to tackle the five-year repair and rebuild plan. The Stronger Christchurch Infrastructure Rebuild Team, more commonly known as Scirt, is run on a collaborative basis. A team made up of staff from each of the organisations assigns jobs to each contractor.

Despite the emphasis on teamwork, there is still a competitive bite to the arrangement. Companies are awarded contracts through what has been described as a carrot and stick system — contractors who complete jobs on time, and to a high standard, receive bonuses and more work, while those who fail to perform are cut out of the action and face financial penalties.

In May 2012, Watercare Auckland boss Mark Ford was shoulder-tapped to oversee the rebuild and communication between the official agencies as chairman of Scirt's client governance group. Ford, who is best known for leading the Super City merger of Auckland in 2009, said shortly after his appointment that he had been attracted to the role by the size and scale of the rebuilding effort.

'I love difficult jobs, and this is a difficult job . . . it's about the complexity, working with communities, getting buy-in and delivering on time.'

The alliance is running its own training programme to recruit workers for the rebuild, and is set to put about 900 people through six- to 14-week courses or on-the-job training.

Since its inception, Scirt has largely worked backstage. The alliance's work has been remarkably controversy-free, escaping the barbs fired at CERA and its central city unit from opposition politicans and the general public. In part, this is due to the benign nature of infrastructure. As Mulder points out, it is difficult to politicise the construction of polyethylene pipes and the design of new pumping stations.

'This is infrastructure, it can't be disputed. It's an engineering issue, it's not aesthetic or anything else. Everyone knows it has to be done, and everyone is committed to getting it done.' That attitude is behind a promising start to the infrastructure rebuild.

As of November 2012, the alliance had already completed 223 projects worth $91 million, including 77 kilometres of sewage pipes and 111,157 square metres of road pavement. Another $228.1 million of work was under way, while more than $1.2 billion worth of projects were either being estimated or designed.

The process has not been without its problems. Haggling between the council, the government and insurers about how the rebuild costs were being shared has at times caused fissures. In October 2012, government concerns about whether the council could meet its 40 per cent share of the infrastructure rebuild costs led Finance Minister Bill English to excoriate the council, saying it had failed to open its books and allow the government to plan a solution.

Council chief executive Tony Marryatt rebuffed the criticism in an interview with *The Press*, saying that English's concerns were misplaced given the council's sound strategy. The council's infrastructure insurance cover also hit the headlines, with a $196 million shortfall in its underground infrastructure insurance and concerns about potential undervaluation of council facilities.

Ford acknowledged that the lack of funds for immediate repairs was slowing down work, but said the scale of the disaster had made it difficult for officials to keep up with the costs. 'We could go faster if there was money, but the commitment from the government in Christchurch was fantastic — this is a huge amount of money.'

The large costs are in part due to the decision in many cases to improve the city's infrastructure when reinstating it, rather than simply returning it to its pre-quake state. Worn-down and dated equipment in the city's networks has been replaced with brand-new materials, using the most advanced engineering techniques.

Orion is reinforcing its power cables with concrete as they are relaid to counteract ground movement in a future earthquake, while the city's sewerage pipes are also benefiting from the introduction of vacuum pump stations and pressure wastewater systems in quake-prone areas. Officials say those improvements will future-proof Christchurch's infrastructure and allow it to match politicians' ambitions to transform the city into a 21st-century metropolis.

Christison said the ferocity of the earthquake helped officials identify the most vulnerable points in the city's infrastructure and bring them up to scratch so they were more likely to withstand any future disaster. 'Earthquakes are ruthless at finding the weak spots . . . and when you take the weak spots out, that strengthens the whole network.'

That optimism has extended, if somewhat cautiously, to discussions of whether Scirt will meet its repair deadline of late 2016. Mulder said there was 'no indication that that is unrealistic', but warned that the goalposts could shift if ongoing inspections uncovered further damage.

'We don't know fully the scope of this job, because we haven't done all of the investigation and we haven't seen all of the damage yet.'

Ford was similarly bullish, but said the scale of the programme meant delays were not impossible.

'We're doing everything we can to put it back together, but it comes back to availability of funds. We're ahead of target, but it's really about affordability and the resources to do that extra work.'

One thing all the officials can agree on, however, is that the disruption for Cantabrians is far from over. As Ford has said, 'Traffic jams show progress' — the delays and diversions mean roads are being ripped up while new pipes and pavement are relaid. That the conspicuous delays may obscure the development of the repair plans is almost fitting.

Christchurch's infrastructure may continue to slip beneath the radar of many residents, but the work going on beneath the ground will continue to build a better, stronger city for future generations. ■

# BUSINESS

## A STORY OF SURVIVAL AS BUSINESSES PICK THEMSELVES UP

*Marta Steeman*

The 6.3 magnitude earthquake on February 22, 2011 dealt a huge blow to the Christchurch business community. It destroyed large tracts of the centre of the city and sent about 5700 businesses, with 51,000 employees, fleeing the seismic violence. Two years on, it's still common to find people asking where firms are located if they haven't been in contact with them for a while.

**THE CBD BUSINESSES** were typical of any city centre — speciality shops and retail of various kinds, cafes, restaurants, nightclubs, massage parlours, pubs and bars, backpackers, food shops and wholesale stores. The bigger organisations in the CBD included hotels, bank headquarters, government departments, local authorities, department stores, and many professional firms of lawyers, accountants, architects and IT specialists.

Businesses in the east of the city, particularly in the industrial suburbs of Bromley and Woolston, were also hard hit. The large ones, and even the smaller firms that were well insured and had reserves to fall back on, have picked themselves up and are back on their feet. Some are moving west and south, where industrial-zoned land is available, because their properties are uneconomic to repair.

The thousands of CBD workers and the firms they worked for have settled into various locations in the suburbs or on the fringes of the former central city, and have soaked up any available untenanted spaces. Many people are still working from home. Scores of small CBD businesses have not been re-established, probably in most cases for lack of funds.

A business demography survey by Statistics New Zealand surveyed the locations of Christchurch businesses and the number of their employees a year after the February quake. It showed that overall the numbers of businesses in the city had not declined that much — down by about 900 to

**LEFT** How things used to be. Crowds enjoy outside dining and revelry on The Strip along Oxford Tce on a warm nor'west evening in October 2006.
**DEAN KOZANIC**

**RIGHT** Five years later to the month — demolition and dismantling of the bars and restaurants along The Strip, and now in the red zone, was well under way after they were pounded by the city's quakes.
**DEAN KOZANIC**

36,400 in February 2012. On the face of it that sounds a fairly manageable decline, but it underplays the damage and the casualties.

The tourism sector has been gutted, as has the central city hospitality trade. Many of these are small businesses that lack the resources and connections to survive. Familiar restaurants and cafes, nightclubs and bars have gone. The city's hotel bed stock has been dramatically depleted to about 1000, where pre-quake there were about 3800 beds. The number of international visitors is half what it was three years ago.

The composition of the business community is changing noticeably. Businesses related to building and construction are rising from the rubble. Local companies are expanding and joining forces with overseas partners preparing to pitch for the really big rebuilding projects in a CBD planned by the Canterbury Earthquake Recovery Authority (CERA). The newly minted government department currently rules the roost, in an uneasy partnership with the Christchurch City Council, and will oversee the recovery for the next five years.

Out-of-town operators have set up here and more are expected, not only for the ongoing demolition work but for the construction projects of the future. The building trades are busy repairing damaged homes and constructing some low-rise commercial buildings on the edges of the city and in the suburbs.

Statistics New Zealand's survey illustrates the changing business landscape. The numbers of cafes and restaurants had fallen 20 per cent to 550 by February 2012, while the number of painting and decorating businesses had risen to 470, which was 37 per cent more than a year before. The number of people employed by those businesses had soared 83 per cent to 1200.

House-building companies grew 11 per cent to 1190 by February 2012 and their employees numbered 2200, almost 50 per cent more than a year earlier. Other construction services have expanded similarly, up 14 per cent to 130, with the number of employees up almost 40 per cent as well.

As might be expected after a large natural disaster, insurance business services grew, by 20 per cent, in the year.

The accommodation sector suffered the loss of several large inner-city hotels and a good number of backpacker hostels. The number of employees in the accommodation sector had plunged 35 per cent a year later. However, motels have been enjoying a roaring trade, filled with insurance, engineering and construction-sector employees, who have replaced international tourists.

The western suburbs were much less badly damaged by the February quake, not only because they were further from its epicentre under the Port Hills but because of more stable ground conditions. A year after February 22 the west and southern suburbs had 17,000 more employees working in the construction and hospitality industries, and in professional, scientific and technical services, according to the survey.

Resilience has become the byword for Christchurch, not least for its business community. Canterbury Employers' Chamber of Commerce chief executive Peter Townsend believes the business community has survived battered but not decimated because of its 'sheer bloody-mindedness and determination not to die'.

Part of the main stairwell in the Clarendon Towers collapsed in the February 22, 2011 earthquake, making evacuation of the building a slow process as the city continued being rocked by aftershocks. The building's demolition was completed early in 2013.

**DEAN KOZANIC**

*'I've come to the conclusion that business is actually part of your soul. It's part of what you are. It's part of your family and it's part of your life.'*

'I've come to the conclusion that business is actually part of your soul. It's part of what you are. It's part of your family and it's part of your life. It's your social network. It's your equity. And people did almost anything they could to ensure business survival. They refused to lie down.'

Some took risks that were stupid, admittedly. Hundreds of business owners sneaked into the CBD by night in those early days after the February 22 quake to retrieve files and equipment. Some had connections with the territorial soldiers patrolling the four avenues forming the CBD border who let them in. Aftershocks were still coming thick and fast, rendering many buildings dangerous.

'You look back at some of the risks people took to rescue business support systems and servers out of offices. Nuts. Snuck in in the middle of the night, had a cousin who was working for the territorials, whatever it might be . . . but the reality of that was that people were risking their lives to save their businesses,' Townsend says.

'Could you imagine lining someone up before the earthquakes and asking them, "Would you risk your life for your business?" Of course I wouldn't. You've got to be crazy. Well, hundreds of people did and that really struck me that these businesses mean a lot more to people than just a few dollars.'

Townsend remembers a phone call he took from one of the tenants of Clarendon Towers who wanted to land a helicopter on the roof to retrieve files essential to his business.

'He said, "I just need 20 minutes. Can you arrange it?" I said "You've got to be joking."

'He said "No, I'm hiring a helicopter and I'll land on the roof and I'll whip down and I'll get my deeds and my files out of my office." I said "There's no way." But that was the sort of risks people were prepared to take.

'It's a fascinating story of business survival and it's a lesson for the rest of the world.'

Bruce Gemmell is a managing partner at Ernst & Young in Christchurch, one of the big four accountancy firms. Most of the company's clients are medium to large businesses. Gemmell says the 'big end of town' has come through quite well. Professional services and major financial institutions uprooted from the CBD are capable of relocating quickly and achieving a restart in other locations.

While Christchurch has some top-class companies in the IT, electronics and manufacturing sectors, it remains essentially a very large rural services centre, a huge food producer and commodity exporter. Good commodity prices for dairy and other primary products as well as mineral products cushioned the impacts post-February 22, Gemmell says.

Companies in the roading, underground infrastructure and demolition game have been reaping the benefits in the first two years since the quake. The many trades involved in house repairs are also enjoying the busiest times since the 2008 recession. That's the silver lining for the 'boom–bust' home-building sector.

Gemmell recalls that the first few weeks post-February 22 were 'quite primal'. 'It was for a wee while the survival of the fittest. The quicker you moved the better the outcome.' He says the people who found ways to get into the cordoned-off central city to get their gear out, and who were prepared to take risks, got back on their feet and were operating far more quickly than those who accepted the processes being established by authorities or those who had a zero tolerance for risk.

Most former CBD businesses are still working in inferior conditions in the suburbs, with less space, less comfort and a greater degree of isolation from clients and their peers. Many have shifted at least a couple of times.

The scramble to secure premises after February 22 was frantic. Rumours swirled of a government department that grabbed a building sight unseen. Untenanted space in some new commercial buildings in the suburb of Addington, just southwest of the centre, was snapped up in 48 hours. Space at commercial office parks in northwestern suburbs like Burnside filled with displaced law and accountancy firms within days, and banks retreated to suburban branches and squeezed their teams in there.

Two of the city's biggest telecommunications players had several hundred people working from home while they scoured the city for premises and began emergency repairs on their networks. Telecom had to find digs for more than a thousand staff who had been working at its headquarters in Hereford St, in the heart of the CBD. Firms in the west that had suffered little damage took in others less fortunate. Tait Electronics, one of Christchurch's largest businesses, provided refuge to several other firms. Lounges, spare bedrooms and garages became places of work. One of the big four

TOP Canterbury Chamber of Commerce chief executive Peter Townsend said people did 'almost anything' to ensure their businesses would survive following the quakes, hundreds sneaking into the central city at night in the days after February 22, 2011, to collect files and equipment.
CARYS MONTEATH

MIDDLE TOP Knowing that access would quickly become a problem, this businessman carries a computer under each arm as he walks down a badly damaged central city street just minutes after the magnitude 6.3 quake on February 22, 2011.
JOHN KIRK-ANDERSON

MIDDLE BOTTOM Computer equipment is recovered from a collapsed building in Cashel St following the earthquake.
JOHN KIRK-ANDERSON

BOTTOM Rolleston's population growth has accelerated since the quakes as Christchurch people move out into the Selwyn District and its more stable ground.
DEAN KOZANIC

accountancy firms, KPMG, occupied a church for a short time. Trade plummeted immediately after February 22 as all firms took stock. But it never came to a complete standstill, because the west and south of the city were much less damaged than other areas.

Peter Townsend says a couple of the key reasons businesses survived was the behaviour of the banks and the taxman, the Inland Revenue Department (IRD). The banks provided additional cash to companies and increased working capital, and they forwent loan repayments and paid wages on trust because the companies did not have any records. IRD immediately said provisional tax payments could cease and it would give more time for GST payments.

'Our bank paid wages for my staff for over a month, just based on what they were paying them before the earthquake, because we had no records.' Adjustments were made later on, Townsend says.

'The behaviour of the banks was and still is one of the great reasons why the commercial fabric of our city has been more or less kept intact. And IRD the same.'

However, probably the key reason so many businesses survived was the more than $200 million spent by the government on wage subsidies for businesses for three months after the February quake. At its peak, about 65,000 employees and sole traders at about 6000 businesses — around 20 per cent of the Christchurch workforce — were being supported by the wage subsidies.

'That cash injection provided the companies with cash flow and allowed them to make other decisions about their business,' Townsend says. 'Whereas if they hadn't had that cash they'd be just thinking about survival, and they'd be dying.'

The government had already spent just over $10 million on wage subsidies after the

September 4, 2010 earthquake. 'Post-February 22, [Finance Minister] Bill English rang me on the morning of Feb 23 and he said, "Peter, don't worry, we know this is big, we're going to up the ante on the employment support subsidy, we're going to make it $500 a week instead of $350, it's going to apply to all companies, not just small companies".'

Townsend says the money started rolling into company accounts within two days.

'I have said to John Key, to Bill English, to Gerry Brownlee, to [Social Development Minister] Paula Bennett, to anyone who will listen to me, next time there is a major disaster in New Zealand you pump cash into companies on a high-trust basis straight away because it saves companies and it saves an enormous cost on the community.

'If that hadn't happened, post-February in particular, we would have had devastation. The commercial fabric of our city would have been destroyed and we would not be where we are today, because the people would be on their knees, not on their feet.'

The government used a similar mechanism to support some companies after the *Rena* shipping disaster, he says.

'I think there were some really valuable lessons learned that have national ramifications. And my understanding was the abuse of the system was minimal.' Audit work revealed the fraud rate was lower than the normal unemployment benefit fraud.

Townsend is an extraordinarily optimistic character, and his enthusiasm is persuasive. 'People say to me, "Why are you so optimistic?" I say, "What is the other bloody choice?".'

The flow-on effects for local businesses are going to be huge during the rebuild, but at this early stage it is still a bit beyond the comprehension of most people, he says.

The ranks of the unemployed had been expected to swell by tens of thousands in Christchurch after February 22, but that never happened to the extent feared. However, unemployment did rise to levels not seen for several years. Canterbury had enjoyed low levels of unemployment during the building boom of the mid-2000s, and in September 2010 the unemployment rate stood at 4.8 per cent, with some 16,900 people unemployed in the region, according to the Household Labour Force Survey. Six months later, by the end of March 2011, the unemployed numbered 22,600, an unemployment rate of 6.4 per cent.

That tapered off over 2011, but rose again to 6.5 per cent in June 2012 as the fuller effects of the earthquakes emerged and business interruption insurance expired for a number of firms. A CERA economics report estimated a higher unemployment rate in Christchurch of about 7.5 per cent by mid-2012.

**TOP LEFT** Telecom customer service representative Stacey Park works at the call centre set up in her Edgeware flat with her manager Frank Smits.
**JOHN KIRK-ANDERSON**

**TOP RIGHT** Thank goodness for the billiard table. Lawry Hanafin, right, and his wife Jacquie make good use of the large green baize surface as a makeshift office.
**DAVID HALLETT**

**MIDDLE** Don Rutter leaves hairdresser Joanne Beardsley's new Winters Rd premises on a sunny day in May 2011. The Chancery Lane business is just one of several hairdressers that relocated to suburban garages as a result of the quakes.
**DEAN KOZANIC**

**BOTTOM LEFT** Hairy Lemon staff hold a meeting in the crowded office of Sue Wilkinson, front. From left, Whitney Cox, Lucinda McCullough, Tom Shand and Briony Bonisch.
**JOHN KIRK-ANDERSON**

**BOTTOM RIGHT** Duns chartered accountants senior partner Glenn Staply said staff were happy with their new premises in Moorhouse Ave, despite rather cramped conditions.
**CARYS MONTEATH**

BARBER SHOP OPEN

In addition, some building firms laid off staff after gearing up for quite a bit more work in 2012 then finding that it did not eventuate. That was because insurers were not covering new buildings, and the Earthquake Commission and insurers were still arguing over how to apportion damage between them, which also slowed down repairs.

The numbers of unemployed have gradually declined, and by September 2012 stood at 17,500, a 5.2 per cent unemployment rate, much lower than the national rate of 7.3 per cent.

The Household Labour Force Survey also reveals that the Canterbury workforce shrank quite a lot in the months after the February 2011 quake as hundreds of people left the region, mostly for Auckland, other South Island towns, or Australia. More women lost their jobs than men because of the loss of many hospitality businesses and the closing of international language schools. About 15,000 fewer women were employed in September 2012 than two years earlier, as opposed to about 4000 fewer men.

**ELECTRONICS FIRM AUCOM** is an example of a Christchurch manufacturer whose business was affected relatively lightly revenue-wise but, like most other firms, had employees who were traumatised by the long series of quakes. Managing director Brent Archer says the Addington factory closed on Tuesday, the day of the quake, and after building assessments for safety was back in production by Friday. Neither sales nor customers were lost.

Despite the quakes, Christchurch company Aucom Electronics maintained its strong exports in industrial power controls to several countries, including Turkey. On June 29, 2011, chief executive Brent Archer, centre, met with Turkish business delegates Rustem Keles, left, Ahmet Demir and Ahmet Hamdi Alpaslan, and Sinan Ketencioglu of Aucom Turkey.
**STACY SQUIRES**

With the help of funding from government agency New Zealand Trade and Enterprise (NZTE), Aucom decided to bring some prospective customers from a Turkish water company to Christchurch to reassure them that the company was operating okay and give them confidence it could still deliver on a $4 million order.

'They got the jitters about "Will you be able to supply? We've seen this city flattened".'

NZTE provided funding to other export businesses for the same reason, to reassure overseas customers that Christchurch companies could meet their contracts. Archer says the biggest threat was the disruption and damage at the smaller businesses that supplied Aucom with sheet metal. They were in the eastern suburbs, and other companies in the wider region rallied around to support them, so supply was not disrupted too much.

The highest priority was to provide a safe environment and some kind of regularity for staff, and allow them time to sort out issues with their families and damaged homes. 'It took a long time, 18 months actually, before the fear of the earthquakes themselves pretty much subsided for most people in our business. What is now providing stress is getting your house rebuilt, dealing with EQC — your life is just busier than it was before.

'The bigger issue for us is the European crisis. The euro is incredibly weak and also some of the business coming out of there is depressed. So that's put pressure on us because 60 per cent of our business is in euros. And so that's our challenge. We are still getting the same level of business, and in fact may be getting a little bit more than two years ago, but it's worth less, which really puts the squeeze on, so we have to work harder and smarter.'

Only recently has Archer been able to take time for himself.

'Just in the last couple of months I've taken up white-water kayaking. I went to Murchison for four days and I felt like myself again. All of a sudden you didn't think about work, you were learning something that hasn't been possible for the last couple or three years. So it was really refreshing to have a life outside of the business and stuff that went on here.'

ONE OF THE city's biggest retailers, Smiths City Group, abandoned its badly damaged Colombo St store on the afternoon of February 22, 2011. The 100-odd staff in the city headquarters decamped a week later to Sockburn, a suburb in the west of Christchurch where the company had administrative premises — a fairly basic two-storey office building and a house. The staff squeezed into the place, which as well as providing work space had laundry, bathroom and shower facilities for staff whose homes were without power and water. There was also a crèche.

'Welcome to the crack house,' chief executive Rick Hellings said when *The Press* visited to check it out. The rather modest house has now become the headquarters of the South Island retail chain, which has 300 administration and sales staff in Christchurch and another 400 around the rest of the South Island and across the lower North Island. A lick of paint turned the pink walls of the house to a more suitable neutral, a fax and copy machine sits in the kitchen, and there's a table for meetings in what was once a bedroom. Hellings expects to remain at Sockburn till at least 2014, when the lease expires, but there is still a question mark over whether the company will be able to rebuild its head office at the city south site under the new blueprint for central city redevelopment.

Fortunately, after the February quake Civil Defence was desperate to reopen the Pak 'n Save supermarket on Moorhouse Ave, which meant clearing the street next to Smiths City. Hellings and a couple of others were allowed into their building and grabbed as much as necessary to keep the business ticking over. He also gave instructions for all the same advertisements to go into the South Island regional papers as the week before. In his view, keeping trading was the key to survival, as was conveying that it was business as usual everywhere else. All staff received a standard pay packet at least until systems were restored.

When Christchurch staff turned up on February 28 at Sockburn, management pledged that no one would be made redundant but said everyone would have to muck in and do all sorts of jobs, regardless of what their contract of employment said. Hellings says one of the men broke down in tears.

One by one the four Christchurch stores under the Smiths City brands were reopened within a month. The Colombo St department store was off-limits behind the cordon until July 2011, and

a big repair job, but it too opened, at last, in November that year. Hundreds of people queued at the door for the grand opening and the bargains. In December 2012 the Group's brand new Powerstore and Furniture Concepts stores on Moorhouse Ave opened their doors, getting on for two years after February 22's destruction.

Hellings recalls driving home toward Huntsbury on the evening of February 22 and seeing a queue outside Barrington Super Liquor. He laughs loudly at an abiding memory. 'And I thought good on you, boys. I thought, it just goes to show that people want to make life as normal as possible.'

**THERE ARE MANY** stories that reflect the gutsiness of Christchurch business owners in getting their firms back up and running.

Veronica Drexel is one gutsy lady. When the earthquake shook its way across Christchurch from its epicentre close to the Heathcote Valley, Drexel was making pizza dough. While her Pizzeria building on Waimairi Road in the west suffered minimal damage, the restaurant lost power and water. Drexel raced home to get the generators they used to run the mobile pizza bus and hooked them up.

By 4.30pm, about 50 locals were knocking on the door asking if the restaurant was serving food. One of her four staff, second-year university student Sophie MacDonald, responded to her request for a hand and together they served 75 pizzas, stopping only at 8pm because they had run out of ingredients. She also took IOUs for those who only had cards but no cash.

The earthquakes have been a double-edged sword for others. When the 300 *Press* newspaper staff decamped after February 22 to the company's print production site on Johns Rd, Harewood, near Christchurch International Airport, Darren Carlow and his espresso coffee and food van ensured all the caffeine addicts were adequately fuelled. Business was booming, but Carlow had to be up at the crack of dawn at the North Beach bakery and then on the road for hours to take advantage of it. Suddenly the suburbs were brimming with hungry workers looking for coffee and lunch, and Carlow was driving across the city to 20 sites each day.

Nearly two years later, he says the path ahead is not as rosy. 'We're going all right, but we are not as busy as we were.' Carlow and business partner Andrew Snee face the prospect of their bakery closing because it needs significant repairs. And if that isn't enough, trade is falling at his cafe at Waimairi Beach in the east of Christchurch. Families in the nearby residential red zone are finally getting their payments from the government and insurers, and his regulars are drifting away to homes in other parts of the city.

Carlow and Snee have to adapt, and they are. They have bought and fitted out a second van to pick up more of the mobile trade that's on offer from the thousands of staff, dislocated from the CBD, who still inhabit offices in the suburbs where food offerings are not necessarily conveniently close.

The tourism industry has taken a big hit. It's a disparate sector with many small businesses. Owners have retrenched: some have closed, some have reduced staff hours, and others have laid off staff. Award-winning small tourism operator Mark Gilbert made a deliberate decision to expand. He felt he had to do something dramatic or fold after the earthquakes.

Gilbert's business, Hassle-free Tours, ran alpine safaris that included a jet-boat ride up the Waimakariri River, a trip to a high-country sheep station and back by train to Christchurch, another trip to a *Lord of the Rings* location site, Edoras, on Mount Potts Station at the head of the Rangitata River in South Canterbury, and a bus tour around the city.

While the September 2010 earthquake scared off some tourists and caused a 10 per cent drop in business by January 2011, the February 22 quake halted it in its tracks. 'Our income just stopped. We lost 80 per cent of our business overnight.' The government's wage subsidy was a lifeline. 'It just allowed us time to think what approach we were going to take.'

Gilbert had always liked the idea of a double-decker bus and it seemed somehow suitable for Christchurch, touted by some as the most English of

While some tourism businesses faced hard decisions after the quake, some closing or retrenching as visitor numbers fell, others, including Hassle-free Tours, saw it as an opportunity. Managing director Mark Gilbert ended up investing in double-decker buses for tours of the city.

**KIRK HARGREAVES**

New Zealand's cities. So he scoured New Zealand and ended up twisting the
arm of the North Island owner of a 1964 London Routemaster, who agreed to
sell him the vehicle. It needed a significant makeover, and they even sourced
the original seat fabric from the United Kingdom to give it authenticity. Now
they have three double-deckers, one open-top bus, which passengers say
they love, and a few other vehicles. The double-decker trips focus on the city
and surrounding areas, and are used as much by locals for events and parties
as by tourists.

Gilbert borrowed to pay for the extra vehicles, and while he won't reveal
who he borrowed from or how much, he says it has been 'challenging', to put
it mildly. 'What I could see was that if we did nothing, we were going to go
broke. If we just tried to carry on with what we were doing, we wouldn't be
able to survive.'

He has also taken advantage of the cruise-ship trade to restore revenue.
With the berth for cruise ships at the Port of Lyttelton badly damaged,
Akaroa has been hosting more than 80 ships during the summer months and
Gilbert has been offering trips around Banks Peninsula.

Before the earthquakes, about 90 per cent of his customers were from
overseas. These days they account for about 35 per cent of business, with
65 per cent domestic tourists and locals enjoying days out.

It's been a tough two years and the business is not yet back to profitability,

but Gilbert is confident it will be in the black in 2013. He says he had to take a longer-term view and recognise that the first two years would be pretty bleak, but being a glass-half-full sort of guy he's hopeful tourism will rise in three or four years.

'There's nothing more rewarding than taking people out and showing them around our beautiful city and our beautiful country. And people will want to come and see this amazing new city that is going to be built.'

Gilbert's infectious optimism is backed up by data released by Statistics New Zealand in late 2012. It shows that the decline in visitor numbers has been arrested and the number of Australian visitors, the single biggest market, is starting to climb. The number of international tourists from major Asian markets and from the United States was also growing again in late 2011.

The biggest psychological boost for the tourism sector came when travel book publisher *Lonely Planet* singled out Christchurch as one of its top 10 destinations. 'Christchurch is bouncing back with a new energy and inventiveness,' *Lonely Planet* said; 'The recovery effort is well under way and 2013 will be an intriguing year to join the rebirth of this proud southern city.'


**THE INFORMATION AND** technology sector appears to have been one of the more resilient. Owen Scott, of IT marketing company Concentrate, reckons the impact of the earthquakes on the IT sector has been limited. Many companies were 'exporters' with customers out of Christchurch so their trade was unaffected, though their people were. Concentrate's yearly survey of IT businesses shows them to be growing, and the sector seems to be coping fairly well in an earthquake-damaged city, Scott says.

Concentrate shifted several times in the 18 months following the February 22 quake, and in November 2012 finally came to rest at the spanking new Epic (Enterprise Precinct and Innovation Campus) hub in Tuam St. That part of town has been designated the IT and Innovation Precinct in the new central city 'blueprint'.

The Epic hub is housed in a new temporary building that has a big-shed exterior and a cool, funky interior. The building is a collaborative project between the Christchurch City Council and the IT sector, supported by BNZ Bank and other large city businesses. It is home to 18 IT firms.

'I know just in our little business we never actually unpacked. And now we are,' Scott says. 'We had been on trestle tables for a year. We've got rid of our rubbish, and we are back in business. It's quite a good feeling actually.'

And the company is enjoying having more visitors again. 'It's one of the biggest issues I think you have in the industry. You don't know where everyone is. And you had to go out of your way to have a meeting,' Scott says.

**SOMEWHAT SURPRISINGLY, THE** number of insolvencies caused by the earthquakes has not been as large as first expected. In fact, Keiran Horne, an insolvency specialist with accountants and business advisors HFK, says insolvencies dropped off after the quakes.

Horne believes there are several reasons for this, one of which is 'creditor compassion'. IRD put an instant halt to liquidation proceedings in Canterbury for quite some time after the February quake, although that has now been lifted. Other creditors gave those in debt more leeway, including banks, which stopped chasing clients.

'There is no way that a bank would have put a Canterbury company into receivership in those months after the earthquake. You can imagine the headlines. They are just so aware of the reputational risk these days,' Horne says.

Insurance companies have not been regarded as friendly parties by many in the business community who have battled the big players over interpretations of business interruption insurance and huge increases in commercial insurance premiums. 'I think the biggest thing is, though, that the insurance proceeds have made businesses liquid,' Horne says.

Those struggling businesses with adequate cover found the insurance payments actually enabled them to settle their debts. 'And that insurance payout in many cases would have been better than they would have got in a fire-sale situation. There's a lot of money that has come in, and is yet to come in, that has stimulated the economy.'

Of course there have also been a good number of companies that have been placed in liquidation with insurance issues still to resolve. 'We have obviously had some appointments that were a direct result of the earthquakes — don't get me wrong, we have — but nowhere near the number we anticipated.'

Horne says that from a pure economic perspective the earthquake has sorted out the weak players and left the resources for the stronger ones to continue. Those stronger businesses have become a lot more efficient since the quakes, and also more innovative about how they work.

Horne used her own job as an example of that. She says she used to travel a lot, but she can now work using Skype video conferencing, as boardroom space is at a premium and travelling across the city is harder, while she is also set up to work from home when she wants.

**DATA GATHERED BY** CERA's Christchurch Central Development Unit (CCDU) from several research houses estimated that the September earthquake decreased economic output by about 2.5 to 3 per cent, and the February earthquake shrank the regional economy a further 6 per cent, the equivalent of a severe recession. 'The combined total impact over the September 2010–June 2011 period was a decline in output of about 8 per cent to 11 per cent,' CCDU reported.

The post-earthquake economic shrinkage bottomed out in late 2011, and since then the Canterbury economy has been in recovery. CERA's general manager of economic recovery, Steve Wakefield, said in November 2012 with the release of the *Economic Recovery Programme for Greater Christchurch* that the region's economic activity was back to pre-September 2010 levels. Canterbury was the fastest growing region in the country for several months of 2012. And the ANZ Bank estimated that the regional economy grew 5.1 per cent in the year to September 2012.

Other positive indicators illustrate the recovery is well under way. Canterbury's population stopped shrinking in October 2012, with positive inward migration recorded that month. The region continues to be a major source of new jobs, CERA reports, and strong growth in the agricultural hinterland continues to support the city. Christchurch is now poised for a reconstruction on a scale it is hard to get your head around.

Over the past two years the estimated cost of the post-earthquake rebuilding project has been something of a moving feast. At the end of 2012, the Reserve Bank gave the official tick to a recovery cost of $30 billion, a figure the local pundits had been predicting 18 months before.

To put it in perspective, $30 billion is 15 per cent — or one-seventh — of all the goods and services this small country produces each year — our gross domestic product. So the economic stimulus is going to be huge locally, and will also underpin the country's economic growth for a few years.

In its *Budget Policy Statement 2013*, the government forecast that the Christchurch rebuild will contribute 0.7 per cent a year to growth over the next few years. That is almost 30 per cent of New Zealand's total forecasted growth coming from the rebuild.

Employers' Chamber of Commerce chief executive Peter Townsend reckons the reconstruction cost will be closer to $40 billion, and that the bulk of that money will be spent here in the next 10 to 15 years. He says some economists are saying there is no net benefit to the city because it is just replacing what has been lost.

'That's absolute rubbish. We will be the recipients of about $30 billion. That's new money building new things, creating new jobs.'

Christchurch will not be going back to where it was.

'That's what excites me and gets me up in the morning.' ∎

**TOP LEFT** Cranes have popped up all over central Christchurch to support building demolition and reconstruction. This one was working at 83 Victoria St on January 17, 2012.
**DEAN KOZANIC**

**TOP RIGHT** The Ibis Hotel in Hereford St was the first to reopen to guests after the quakes. Kaye Scales-Thain puts the finishing touches to one of the rooms looking out over empty sites to the back of the Re:Start Container Mall in Cashel St.
**DAVID HALLETT**

**BOTTOM** It's hard to believe this was once one of the city's best eating and drinking spots. The Strip on Oxford Tce currently lies empty, with the buildings at right and in the centre having been demolished towards the end of 2012.
**JOHN KIRK-ANDERSON**

# SPORT
## AIMING HIGH

*Tony Smith*

An intimate amphitheatre at Addington became
Christchurch's Field of Dreams and a shining symbol
of the city's post-earthquake rebuild.

**IN THE CELLULOID** *Field of Dreams*, Hollywood's baseball-as-a-metaphor-for-life movie, Ray Kinsella (played by Kevin Costner) heard voices in his cornfield: 'If you build it, he will come.' 'He' was Kinsella's dearly departed, distant dad, but also Shoeless Joe Jackson and other disgraced baseballers from the Chicago White Sox who were banned for life for pocketing bribes to throw the 1919 World Series.

Kinsella's task was a doddle — all he had to do was cut down his cornstalks and create a dirt diamond. Contrast that with the task faced by Canterbury Earthquake Recovery Minister Gerry Brownlee, the Canterbury Earthquake Recovery Authority (CERA) and Canterbury's territorial authorities.

The February 2011 earthquake crippled the city's sporting sector. Christchurch's two defining and internationally recognised sporting arenas — Queen Elizabeth II Stadium, built in North New Brighton for the 1974 Commonwealth Games, and Waltham's AMI Stadium, formerly Lancaster Park where elite sport had been played since 1881 — were both destroyed. Downstream effects were deleterious for both amateur and elite sport.

At QE II, the track where Canterbury's Dick Tayler won the Commonwealth Games gold medal was a buckled wreck. Water slopped from the pool where Mark Treffers and Jaynie Parkhouse swam to Commonwealth titles in 1974, and High Performance Sport New Zealand's Christchurch training base was also ruined. AMI Stadium — the South Island's largest sporting venue, with 38,500 seats — was declared structurally unsound just a year after a $60 million redevelopment. Its pristine pitch became a gloopy, gluggy quagmire, riddled with silt from quake liquefaction.

Faced with nowhere to play, the International Rugby Board and New Zealand organising committee confirmed in March 2011 that they were shifting seven 2011 Rugby World Cup

matches — five pool games and two quarter-finals — from Christchurch. The news, though much anticipated, was still a psychological and financial hammerblow.

The February 22, 2011 earthquake struck just three days after the Crusaders' first game in the Super 15 rugby campaign. With AMI Stadium out of action, the Crusaders became rugby's cuckoos, roosting in rivals' nests or forced to play at smaller provincial venues. Todd Blackadder's team spent the entire season on the road, playing 'home' games in Nelson, Timaru, Napier, Wellington and even London, where their match against the Sharks was the first Super Rugby fixture played in the northern hemisphere.

Yet the Crusaders produced the brand of resilience and courage in the face of adversity that stricken householders, Farmy and Student Army volunteers, and fluorescent-vested rescue workers were displaying daily at home. They made the Super 15 final, only to be beaten in Brisbane by the Queensland Reds, whose own backyard had been blitzed by major floods in January 2011.

The Crusaders, who had made a surplus of $125,714 in 2010 (still a far cry from the $2 million profits reaped in the early 2000s), registered a record $696,300 loss in 2011.

The Canterbury Rugby Football Union's (CRFU) bank balance also took a hit. It was forced to move Canterbury's national provincial championship games from AMI Stadium to Rugby Park in Malvern St, St Albans, where the seating capacity was a skinny 7000. Canterbury went on to win a fourth consecutive title but gate revenue dropped by 79 per cent to $220,000 (from $1.04 million in 2010). The CRFU suffered a record $563,142 deficit, although chief executive Hamish Riach expressed hope a successful business interruption insurance claim would soften the financial blow.

But the message was loud and clear. A new home was needed for the province's flagship sports teams. Without a stadium, Christchurch could say goodbye to hosting an All Blacks test, an All Whites football international or a rugby league match featuring the Warriors or the Kiwis.

A temporary stadium was mooted at Addington's Rugby League Park, a significant sporting venue in Christchurch for more than a century and once the base for the region's Agricultural and Pastoral Show. But before anything could be done, the Canterbury Rugby Football League (CRFL), which held an iron-clad lease on Rugby League Park, had to sanction a change in conditions. Rugby union and rugby league had been at odds for more than a hundred years after an infamous split in England in 1895.

A deal was struck which saw the CRFL retain the lease but agree to allow construction of a 17,500-seat stadium, with the Crusaders and Canterbury rugby teams as anchor tenants. New Zealand Rugby League saw it as a chance 'to not only work for the long-term benefit of league', chief executive Jim Doyle said, 'but also to assist the sporting community in Canterbury which has suffered so much as a result of the earthquakes.'

CRFL chairman Ian Jenkins agreed: 'Rugby league's been played on this ground for 60 years and this stadium means it will be played there for many years to come.'

But the stadium would not have become a reality without Minister Brownlee and Prime Minister John Key waving their magic wands. The government agreed to underwrite the cost — eventually $30 million — with funding support from the Canterbury Earthquake Appeal Trust, the Christchurch City Council, the New Zealand Rugby Union and corporate sponsorship. Naming rights were later secured by AMI Insurance, sponsors of the damaged stadium in Waltham. Governance was vested in a Christchurch Stadium Trust chaired by Brownlee and Key's former political rival, ex-Alliance party leader and longtime Christchurch constituency MP Jim Anderton.

AMI Addington Stadium was built in 100 days between mid-November 2011 and March 2012, when it hosted its first Super Rugby match. The whirlwind speed of construction stunned sporting sector insiders. Riach was

a frequent site visitor during the giddy development stages. 'Looking back, it's a little bit surreal,' he said in December 2012. 'The first 23 days were spent knocking down the [two] old stands, so the actual construction phase was less than 100 days.'

Riach reckoned the construction staff were working on 'more than a stadium for the city and a home for the Crusaders'. 'It was a symbol of something much greater, a demonstration of the future [of Christchurch], of hope and the rebuild.' It was, Riach said, a 'wonderful example' of what communities can do and what sport is all about.

Positive effects were soon felt. The Crusaders played every home match at the Addington ground in 2012 and went from red to black, recording a modest $87,147 surplus. 'If it weren't for the new AMI Stadium at Addington, this year's surplus would not have been possible,' Crusaders chairman Murray Ellis said in December 2012. 'We are extremely grateful to the government for driving this project and allowing our team to once again play at home in front of Christchurch and Canterbury fans.'

Addington also became the fortress for the Canterbury ITM Cup team, coached by Tabai Matson and captained by George Whitelock, that won a record fifth consecutive national title in 2012.

By season's end, few in the sporting fraternity were still lamenting the loss of the old AMI Stadium. In its Lancaster Park incarnation, that citadel near the old Christchurch Gasworks was a storehouse of magic sporting and cultural moments, hosting countless rugby, cricket, hockey and soccer tests, Peter Snell's 800-metre and 880-yard track world records in 1962, a papal visit in 1986 and numerous rock concerts. But it was a multi-sport venue with an oval perimeter, designed to host both rugby and cricket. Truth be

told, it had become a dog of a place in which to watch football in the professional rugby era, with fans in the stands far removed from the on-field action.

The players would never admit it publicly, but they hated playing there because the atmosphere was almost non-existent. It improved marginally after the 2010 redevelopment, most noticeably when the Wellington Phoenix — with their entourage of noisy Yellow Fever fans — drew crowds of 19,000 and 14,500 for two A-League football matches against Adelaide United.

The new Addington stadium was built as a football venue, with a rectangular field bounded by two main, temporary covered stands and with open stands behind both sets of goalposts. Cantabrian Ben Sigmund reckoned it felt like a real football ground when the Phoenix played a pre-season game there in September 2012. Various All Blacks also remarked that the atmosphere was akin to that experienced in Europe, with supporters almost within touching distance.

Full-house signs went up at several Crusaders games in 2012 and for the All Blacks' knife-edge second test win over Ireland in June. All Whites captain Ryan Nelsen, a long-time English premier league star and now MLS coach, played his first international in hometown Christchurch when he led New Zealand to a 3–0 win over Tahiti in October 2012. That match featured the 200,000th ticket sold at the stadium in its six-month history, prompting Stadium Trust chair Jim Anderton to declare it 'a spectacular success'.

More highlights are on the horizon. All Blacks are slated to play France at AMI Stadium in 2013, and plans are afoot to lure the Warriors there for a pre-season clash with a National Rugby League opponent in 2014.

But Anderton also injected a note of realism in an interview with *The Press*. He said the trust would have to pay $750,000 a year to lease the

stadium seats from 2013. Buying the seats wasn't an option as the stadium had only a four-year lifespan. Anderton also warned that an annual $500,000 insurance bill was looming 'like a screaming train'.

The Addington stadium was designed as a short-term fix for between three and five years. But it will clearly have to suffice until the construction of the new 35,000-seat stadium mooted in the government's Central City Recovery Plan. The arena, which could have a roof, will be erected on the former Turners and Growers site in Tuam St, between Madras and Barbadoes streets. So Canterbury and the Crusaders are comfortably catered for in the medium term. But is the rest of the region's sporting and recreation sector back up off the canvas after the earth's seemingly endless undulations?

Every sporting code in Canterbury was affected to a greater or lesser extent. Rowing and hockey took the first big hits at the time of the 7.1 magnitude September 2010 quake, which obliterated rowing's headquarters at Kerrs Reach on the Avon River. At hockey's spiritual home at Avonside's Porritt Park, two international-quality water-based artificial turfs were destroyed and grass pitches were strafed with silt.

The February 2011 quake brought an abrupt end to summer sports seasons. Canterbury Softball was forced to cancel two major events — the national secondary schools tournament and the annual Southern Cross Challenge series featuring Australian and New Zealand teams. Winter sports, which were due to kick-off in early April, were also seriously

**LEFT** Hometown boy Ryan Nelsen returned from the English premier league to captain the All Whites against Tahiti Nui in a 2014 World Cup Stage 3 qualifiers game. The All Whites won the game on October 16, 2012, two goals to nil.

**JOSEPH JOHNSON**

**MIDDLE** Steam rises from a scrum on a frosty winter's night at Addington's AMI Stadium, as the All Blacks played Ireland in their first Christchurch test for two years on June 16, 2012. A last-minute dropped goal from Dan Carter saw the All Blacks edge ahead 22–19.

**IAIN MCGREGOR**

RIGHT Liquefaction in the February 22, 2011 earthquake ruined the hockey turfs at Porritt Park and put huge pressure on the city's other hockey facilities at St Bede's College and Nunweek Park.
**DON SCOTT**

BOTTOM Lateral spreading along the banks of the Avon River from the violent shaking caused huge damage to the Kerrs Reach rowing facilities.
**DON SCOTT**

impacted by the closure of countless liquefaction-afflicted sportsfields, particularly in the worst-affected eastern suburbs.

The cry from all codes was universal. Sports administrators were keen to get competitions up and running so both junior and senior sportspeople had sport to look forward to each week as an interlude to their daily duels with insurance companies and bureaucracy. Former Sport Canterbury chief executive Geoff Barry played an instrumental role in rallying sports throughout the city. The former New Zealand surf-lifesaving international, who grew up at South Brighton beach, helped form the Canterbury Sport and Recreation Earthquake Leadership Group to liaise with CERA and the region's territorial authorities. Christchurch-based Sport New Zealand official Richard Lindsay was another key player.

In April 2011 Sport Canterbury appointed a sport recovery manager — former Canterbury Squash general manager Vaughan Utteridge — to oversee the recovery process. His initial prognosis was gloomy. Winter sport membership had dropped by 15 per cent, or 8000 people, in 2011, he told *The Press*. 'Many have left town, some for good, while others are unable to get involved in any organised sport given their circumstances.'

Ian Mallard, a long-serving rugby coach, told *The Press* his Linwood club lost '18 out of 45-odd players' from its two top senior teams at the start of the 2011 season. Clearly something had to be done across the board to ensure Canterbury sport remained on top of its game.

The sector's leadership group commissioned a report from the Global Leisure Group, and *Places and Spaces for Sport and Recreation in Greater Christchurch* was published in March 2012. It catalogued the carnage wrought by the quakes and evaluated options for the future.

First and foremost, the report set out the importance of the sport and recreation sector. It drew on research by Lincoln University economics professor Paul Dalziel, a leading Canterbury football referee, for a SPARC (Sport and Recreation New Zealand) study in 2011. Dalziel deduced that sport and recreation contributed as much — $5.2 billion or 2.8 per cent of GDP — to the New Zealand economy in 2008/09 as the dairy industry. The *Places and Spaces* document said sport and recreation contributed $760 million to the Canterbury economy in 2008/09 and employed more than 7000 people, 2.5 per cent of the region's workforce. Some 124,000 Cantabrians were regular sporting volunteers.

The report made sobering reading, detailing, as it did, the exact impact of the quakes on some of the region's most popular sporting venues. Critical losses included AMI Stadium at Waltham, QE II, Centennial Pool, facilities at Kerrs Reach and Porritt Park, and tennis' Wilding Park headquarters. Pioneer and Cowles stadiums, two

*Forty-two of the city's 980 parks used for sports and recreation were still closed in December 2011, and 34 had only limited access.*

of the city's most used indoor sports venues, were commandeered as temporary welfare centres.

Forty-two of the city's 980 parks used for sports and recreation were still closed in December 2011, and 34 had only limited access. The Christchurch City Council closed 105 sports fields immediately after the February quake, with 33 out of bounds for the entire winter season. But only seven to 10 were expected to be permanently off-limits because of sustained liquefaction damage — six of those were at Bexley Park, where Coastal Spirit's football clubrooms were destroyed.

The report revealed that Canterbury had been left without an international all-weather athletics track and a 50-metre swimming pool and water-polo facility due to the loss of QE II. It also had 'compromised' flat water sports training space for rowing and kayaking, no international-quality hockey pitches — meaning no national tournaments or Black Sticks tests could be held in Christchurch — and a severe shortage of indoor basketball and netball courts. Cricket was a major casualty, too, with the loss of its Village Green facility at QE II for first-class fixtures and its test-match arena at AMI Stadium. That meant Christchurch was off the radar for international test, 50-over and Twenty20 cricket, with the 2015 Cricket World Cup tournament looming on the horizon.

The impact wasn't confined to bricks and mortar and grass fields. Some of the city's top sportspeople joined the exodus from Christchurch to access intact training facilities. Beijing Olympic Games heptathlon representative Rebecca Wardell departed for Dunedin to use the Caledonian Ground track and New Zealand Academy of Sport amenities. 'It's a necessity for me to have an all-weather surface to train on in preparation for London,' Wardell told *The Press* at the time.

Wardell was one of eight Canterbury sportspeople, including fellow Olympians Andrea Hewitt (triathlon) and Joanne Kiesanowski (cycling), who received New Zealand Olympic Committee hardship grants in December 2011 to cover costs incurred after the quakes. Triathlete James Elvery, who received $6000, told *The Press*: 'Losing QEII was huge for Christchurch triathletes. I moved back to Christchurch four years ago from Auckland so I could be closer to the training facilities [at QE II], which were the best in the country.'

Unhappily, Wardell's story did not end in a golden glow. The 34-year-old had to retire after suffering a serious hamstring injury a month before the 2012 London Olympic Games.

But Sophie Pascoe's did. The swimming star stayed in Christchurch to train under coach Roly Crichton and went on to win six medals — three gold and three silver — at the 2012 London Paralympics.

The New Zealand Olympic Committee's generosity was matched by other sporting codes, with provincial, national and international bodies offering grants to their Canterbury counterparts. Football, the world's biggest global sport, came to Mainland Football's aid. Mainland chief executive Mike Coggan and chairman Mark Stewart were able to set up a hardship fund with $140,000 funded through Mainland's own reserves and grants from New Zealand Football, the Oceania Football Confederation and the Japanese Football Association. The latter was a particularly generous act considering the damage wrought by Japan's massive earthquake and devastating tsunami in March 2011.

FIFA, world football's governing body, weighed in with a $380,000 solidarity grant in November 2011, in addition to $685,000 donated through the FIFA Goal Project fund toward a new artificial pitch at English Park. The pitch, approved before the earthquakes, was a joint project between Mainland Football and the Christchurch City Council, which contributed more than $1 million to the total $1.8 million cost. Work on the pitch was delayed by the February 2011 quake but it opened in October, with Coggan anticipating it would host over 3000 hours of football each year as opposed to 100 hours on the old grass surface.

Rugby World Cup Limited, organisers of the highly successful 2011 Rugby World Cup tournament in New Zealand, announced a $400,000 donation in January 2012 to assist with the restoration of rugby infrastructure in Canterbury.

Canterbury Basketball, which lost access to half its playing courts after the quakes, received $40,000 from the New Zealand, Oceania and international (FIBA) basketball federations to fund a portable administration base.

Corporate sponsors and individuals put their hands in their pockets too. Crusaders and All Blacks midfielder Sonny Bill Williams was one of the most generous individual donors. Williams, who had been living in Christchurch for less than six months, gave $100,000 from his charity boxing bout purse to the Christchurch earthquake appeal. He beat Alipate Liava'a in The Clash for Canterbury in Auckland in June 2011.

Williams had been sitting in a spa pool at a Christchurch swimming pool when the February 2011 quake hit. 'I thought the roof was going to collapse,' he told a Fairfax Australia journalist.

Canterbury's speedway ace Ivan Mauger, a former multiple world champion, told *The Press* he would donate $1000 per month to the earthquake appeal along with proceeds from the sale of his autobiography, published in 2011.

Kiwis rugby league winger Matt Duffie donated Melbourne Storm

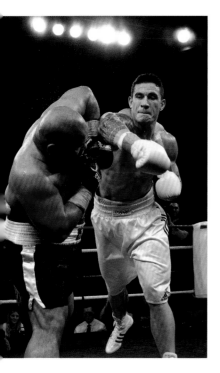

Sonny Bill Williams in dominant form against Alipate Liava'a in 'The Clash for Canterbury' in June 2011. Williams donated $100,000 of his purse to the Christchurch earthquake appeal.

**LAWRENCE SMITH**

memorabilia to an auction to raise money for his former Christchurch club, the Northern Bulldogs, who lost their uninsured clubrooms and their home ground at Kaiapoi's Murphy Park in the September 2010 shake.

Tales of Kiwi sporting ingenuity abounded after the earthquakes. For every athlete forced to quit Christchurch to train and compete, hundreds stayed and found ways to keep in shape. The gymnastics community was left bereft, with only one Christchurch gym remaining open and another damaged but still accessible. But Canterbury men's gymnastics team manager Barbara Price told the *Marlborough Express* before the October 2012 national artistic championships in Blenheim that team members had still managed to train three or four hours a day, six days a week, despite the multitude of aftershocks.

'There have been times after a magnitude 6 aftershock the gym has to shut, so we were just out into the park with the mats or in the children's playground doing chin-ups on the equipment,' Price said.

**REMARKABLY, CANTERBURY SPORTS** teams still managed to taste success in 2011 despite the earthquakes' upheavals. The Canterbury Red Sox men's softball team won their first national title in 15 years just two days before the February 2011 quake, while the Canterbury men's and women's cricket teams and the Canterbury NPC rugby team, to name just a few, also triumphed in 'earthquake season'.

The roll of honour continued in 2012. The new crop of Canterbury champions included the Cats women's hockey team, who won their first national crown for a decade. Canterbury senior and age-group hockey teams claimed six national titles in 2012. That prompted Christchurch-based Black Sticks national assistant coach Chris Leslie to make a comment echoed by colleagues in other codes. 'When you have a catastrophe it makes you stronger as a person and as a group. I think there's a little bit of that in Canterbury hockey. They've pulled together and said, "Stuff it, we may not have had ideal training opportunities but we are probably tougher as a group."'

The Avon Rowing Club, along with other Christchurch clubs, lost their facilities at Kerrs Reach in September 2010. But they won the Centennial Oar for the top-performed club at the national championships soon after the big February shake. Christchurch crews were also dominant at the annual Maadi Cup secondary schools regatta.

Avon also proved a poster club in the post-quake rebuild. An energetic building committee headed by 1984 Olympic Games bronze medallist Don Symon raised almost $1 million for new facilities, with support from the city council, the Fulton Hogan Trust, Christchurch Earthquake Appeal Trust and

New Zealand Community Trust. Two sheds at Kerrs Reach and another at Stewart's Gully on the Waimakariri River were officially opened by Olympic Games gold medallist Mahe Drysdale in December 2012.

Symon, who thanked CERA for allowing rowing clubs to establish new facilities 'in what is basically a red zone', said at the opening: 'No other sport lost total use of its facilities . . . No other sport has replaced in total its facilities.'

Hockey also didn't allow grass (or astroturf in this case) to grow under its feet. Canterbury Hockey's facilities trust, headed by 1976 Olympic gold medallist Selwyn Maister, oversaw the installation of two new artificial pitches at Harewood's Nunweek Park. The city council contributed $1.5 million of the $3.5 million installation costs. The two new turfs, which replace the Porritt Park pair destroyed in September 2010, gave hockey four artificial surfaces in the city, with three at Nunweek Park and another at the combined St Bede's College-Marist Hockey Club facility.

'We are incredibly fortunate to have what we've got here,' Canterbury Hockey chief executive Rod Templeton said in December 2012. 'A lot of sports in Canterbury don't have the ability to have a physical presence [since the earthquakes].'

Tennis and bowls — two of Canterbury's larger summer codes — also sustained severe damage to club complexes on the eastern side of the city

In December 2012 Avon Rowing opened its new Kerrs Reach and Stewarts Gully facilities. Young rower Lewis Kimber was one who watched the speeches from inside the sheds.

**IAIN MCGREGOR**

but were able to keep competitions going because clubs in the west were relatively unaffected and able to share facilities.

Canterbury Tennis chief executive Neil Prior said 'pretty much all the clubs in Christchurch would have been affected', with Sumner, Redcliffs and Shirley among the hardest hit. But he said competitions and tournaments, 'so vital to the on-going health of the sport', had been able to continue at other clubs. Prior hailed the Shirley Tennis Club as 'a tremendous success story in terms of earthquake recovery'. The club — based at Richmond Park in Woodchester Avenue — sustained major damage to nine courts and their clubrooms in February 2011. A court repaired in May 2011 was damaged again during two big aftershocks in June.

Shirley's junior administrator Wayne Turner, a pivotal figure in the rebuild programme, reported on the New Zealand Tennis website in 2012 that the $175,000 repair bill target had been met through grants, fundraising and residual funds. Turner said Shirley had relocated their senior membership to the Edgeware club for the 2011–12 season but continued to run their junior programme at Shirley. 'Our membership at season end was around 240 (down from 280), which is a good result given we border on a significant red zone area.'

But Canterbury Tennis still had big issues to tackle in 2013. The organisation — with almost 8000 registered members and thousands more casual players — has its headquarters at Wilding Park in Avonside's Woodham Rd, a TC3 zone. All 39 courts — indoor and outdoor — were destroyed in the September 2010 quake, were repaired, then destroyed again in February 2011 while Wilding Park was hosting hundreds of players at the International Tennis Federation seniors tournament. Prior now peeks out the window of his office at the former grass centre-court, 'which still looks like a BMX track'.

Canterbury Tennis' coffers took a major hammering through the 'significant revenue loss' from its year-round indoor tennis centre, scheduled to reopen in March 2013. Prior said Wilding Park's future was still a complex issue, with negotiations with insurers and the city council expected to continue in 2013. The Wilding Park Foundation, the incorporated society that owns the park, was due to report back to clubs by April or May.

Bowls also bounced back after most clubs suffered serious damage in the February 2011 quake when, Bowls Canterbury chief executive Colin Reynolds said, 'liquefaction erupted and made mountains on bowling greens.'

'At my own club, Shirley, we barrowed 40 metres of liquefaction off, which was trucked away . . . The clubhouse was yellow-stickered, you could see through the cracks in the concrete block walls.'

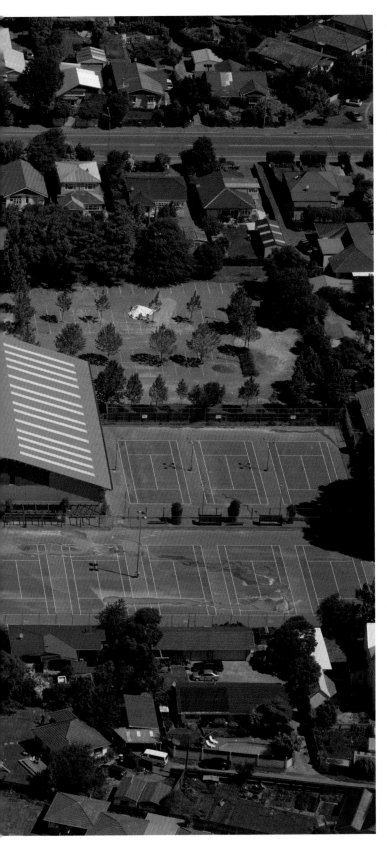

The big December 23, 2011 quakes came as a shock to the city after six months of relative peace. More liquefaction wrecked facilities across the eastern suburbs, including Wilding Park, the home of tennis in the region.

**JOHN KIRK-ANDERSON**

A New Zealand Sport Turf Institute estimate put Shirley's greens repair bill at $63,000, or $1000 per member. 'We only had half that in the bank,' Reynolds said. Members chose to 'call it a day' at their Woodchester St site next to Richmond Park and join other clubs. 'The street was like a bomb site and most of the neighbours were in the red zone.'

Reynolds said Bowls Canterbury now has nine fewer greens, with the closure of Burwood Park (2), Christchurch-Richmond (2), Heathcote Valley, Hornby Workingmen's Club, Kaiapoi Riverside, Mount Pleasant and Shirley. Bowls Canterbury lost 776 players (13.3 per cent of its membership) but Reynolds said it was still one of New Zealand's largest bowling centres, with more than 5000 registered members and 6900 casual players. Entries for interclub and centre events were up 12 per cent in the 2012–13 season.

The impact of the earthquakes had prompted several club amalgamations, with Burwood joining Dallington to form the Avon Park club and Mount Pleasant merging with Redcliffs, where a new synthetic green was being built on the former croquet-green site. Christchurch-Richmond has also relocated to Edgeware and Kaiapoi Riverside has plans for a new complex at Hinemoa Park.

'The earthquake has done some good,' Reynolds acknowledged. 'We still have 62 clubs in Canterbury. Those that have merged are now larger sustainable clubs and those earthquake-damaged clubs have taken their insurance payout with them to a new club, which can look forward to several years of progress with the cash injection.'

**OTHER SPORTS WERE** still in limbo at the turn of 2013. Athletics Canterbury had to relocate to a pine-needle-strewn grass track at Rawhiti Domain after the quake destroyed nearby QE II Stadium. Throwing cages from QE II were retrieved and re-erected, and a steel storage shed was built.

Inter-club meets were held at Rawhiti in tandem with Timaru's Aorangi Stadium, which now has the only synthetic track in Canterbury. Elite athletes voted with their feet, with some, including a stable of hurdlers coached by Jill Morrison, preferring to race only at Aorangi. She wouldn't let her senior athletes 'do hurdles at Rawhiti — even sprint races can be quite dodgy. The risk of injury is too great [on a pitted grass track].'

Athletics Canterbury hatched plans for a new base, with a synthetic track, at the western end of Burnside Park between the Burnside Rugby clubrooms and Roydvale Avenue. In early 2013 the sport was still in talks with rugby officials about the proposal, which is dependent on city council support. Christchurch mayor Bob Parker went in to bat for the proposal in July 2012, recommending the council allocate a total of $6.6 million over two years. But his council amended the recommendation, granting $300,000 for the first year and $6.3 million in the second. Athletics New Zealand official Terry Lomax, a former Canterbury and New Zealand high-jump champion, told *The Press* the decision was 'a kick in the face'.

Top athletics coaches, including Jill Morrison and Andrew Maclennan, have argued track and field needs a new home sooner rather than later because every season that ticks by without a synthetic track to train and race on puts Canterbury athletes at a disadvantage. Maclennan said it was especially important with the Rio de Janeiro Olympic Games looming in 2016.

Canterbury Cricket was also left on the back foot with AMI Stadium at Waltham out of action and QE II's Village Green pitch left a liquefied mess. Canterbury Wizards Plunket Shield first-class matches and limited-over and Twenty-20 games were shifted to Rangiora, but the region still lacked an international venue. By the end of 2012, Christchurch had not hosted a test match for five years or a one-day international for three seasons. Canterbury Cricket chief executive Lee Germon was concerned Christchurch could miss out on hosting 2015 Cricket World Cup matches unless a new home was found.

Germon, a former Black Caps captain, stirred up a hornet's nest with his proposal for a cricket stadium at Hagley Park Oval in the precinct off Deans Ave. Germon went to bat for a stadium capable of hosting up to 20,000 fans, arguing that cricket was an existing use at Hagley Oval where the sport had been played and several clubs had been based for more than a hundred years.

The proposal, featuring floodlights, an embankment, seating and a new pavilion, had heavyweight support. Sir Richard Hadlee, New Zealand's greatest cricketer, told the city council in December 2012 a redeveloped Hagley Oval 'could become an iconic ground . . . and possibly *the* venue in New Zealand for cricket'. Former New Zealand captain Graham Dowling and International Olympic Committee member Barry Maister also added their backing.

But as *The Press* noted in a background article in April 2012: 'You could chisel this line in stone at Christchurch City Council headquarters: "Mess with Hagley Park at your peril".' The article reminded readers of the furore at mayor Ron Guthrey's plan to realign part of Hagley Park at Harper Ave in 1970. He was dumped at the 1971 election.

The Christchurch Civic Trust, the Save Hagley Park group and the Inner City West Neighbourhood group all raised vociferous concern at the park being used as a professional sports venue.

The government listed a redeveloped international cricket ground at Hagley Park as an anchor project in the Central City Recovery Plan, announced in July 2012. But that left the council stuck between a rock and a hard place. *The Press* reported in December 2012 that while the council was responsible for the administration of Hagley Park, under section 23 of the Canterbury Earthquake Recovery Act 2011 the Hagley Park Management Plan, which governs what can happen in Hagley Park, cannot be inconsistent with the Recovery Plan.

Councillors decided in December in a split vote of 10 to 3 to fast-track Canterbury Cricket's consent proposal to the Environment Court rather than appoint an independent commissioner to first consider the matter. The council, mindful that the commissioner's decision would be appealed to the Environment Court, will wait for the court's verdict before deciding whether to grant the cricket body a lease for the Hagley Park Oval.

City councillor Tim Carter said a direct referral to the Environment Court, where those for and against the development could present their case, made sense. 'It's so controversial and there are such strong feelings on it, it will go the Environment Court.'

Canterbury Rugby League, so magnanimous in agreeing to a change in its lease terms to allow the new Addington Stadium to go ahead at Rugby League Park, is another sport that still lacks an enclosed ground to hold premier matches. Its free access to AMI Stadium is restricted to one representative game a year and its club grand finals day.

Canterbury's aquatic sports and indoor codes are holding out for the new Metropolitan Sports Facility proposed in the Central City Recovery Plan. The

A new wicket block is installed at Hagley Oval. Plans to upgrade the oval, in the hallowed ground of Hagley Park, into an international cricket venue have caused controversy around the city.
**DAVID HALLETT**

With other swimming facilities around the city either closed or demolished, pools at Jellie Park in the northwestern suburbs and at Pioneer Pool in the southwest have been stretched to breaking point, particularly during school holidays. This artist's impression shows a new high-performance centre which will be built at Jellie Park.
**PHOTO SUPPLIED**

complex would include a 50-metre, 10-lane swimming pool, pools for diving and water polo, and an eight-court indoor sports arena. The city council initially earmarked the former Red Bus Depot site on the corner of Moorhouse and Fitzgerald avenues as the preferred location. But Sport Canterbury chief executive Geoff Barry warned the council in June 2012 that the site was unsuitable because 'large indoor spaces need to be co-located with green space'. Barry had earlier advocated basing the complex at Hagley Park. But the Christchurch Central Development Unit favoured the site of the now-demolished Canterbury Brewery in Tuam St near South Hagley Park.

Work on the sports complex is scheduled to start by the end of 2013. The new pool will be welcomed by Swimming Canterbury-West Coast, which had to hold its 2012 and 2013 championships at Dunedin's Moana Pool without a 50-metre pool closer to home.

A temporary High Performance Sports centre was due to be opened in March 2013 beside the swimming pool and leisure centre at Christchurch's

Jellie Park. The $3.5 million project, announced by Sports Minister Murray McCully, will have a gym, an indoor sprint track, a full-size netball court, an athletes' lounge and office space for High Performance Sport New Zealand staff. Paralympics swimming star Sophie Pascoe hailed the Jellie Park centre, saying losing the facilities at QE II had been 'hard on all of us'.

**SPORTING HUBS OR** precincts like Jellie Park are expected to sprout in Christchurch. The Places and Spaces plan calls for clusters of 'co-located' sporting facilities and advocates more sports club partnerships like the Westminster Sports set-up in St Albans-Mairehau, and Linfield Sports based around the Linwood Rugby Club in Bromley. It also foreshadowed more facilities sharing with schools — noting the Ministry of Education was a bigger owner of sports facilities in Canterbury than the city council — and tertiary education providers.

The Canterbury sporting public's appetite for major events has not diminished. Most 2012 Super Rugby matches and the All Blacks test at the new AMI Stadium were sold out, with Crusaders and CRFU chief Hamish Riach noting many more seats could have been sold as demand had outstripped supply. Riach believes a new, covered 35,000-seat arena is vital for the future viability of sports like rugby but also as an entertainment hub.

With the Crusaders on the road in 2011, punters sought alternative sporting fixes. Attendance soared at motor-sport venues. Many liked what they saw, and Woodford Glen promoters were anticipating 10,000-plus crowds for major meetings in the 2012–13 season.

Almost 9000 people packed Addington's CBS Canterbury arena in July 2011 to watch a National Hockey League All-stars ice hockey game, despite tickets costing up to $249. And 6000 fans — a record for a basketball match in Canterbury — saw the New Zealand Breakers' pre-season clash with the Wollongong Hawks in September 2012 at the CBS arena. A few weeks later 5000 turned out for the New Zealand–Australia netball test at the same venue.

Participation rates also started to rebuild in 2012 after the 15 per cent across-the-board dip in 2011. Data compiled by Sport Canterbury showed many regional sports organisations reporting significant membership increases. Swimming's numbers increased by 141 per cent, from 387 competitive swimmers in 2011 to 934 in 2012, although still well short of the 1565 figure in 2010. Double-digit rises were also recorded by badminton, bowls, gym sports and volleyball, but netball numbers were down by 17 per cent across the region (which also covers South Canterbury, Mid-Canterbury and the West Coast) and yachting and surf lifesaving were also still struggling.

Crusaders players — including Sean Maitland, right, and George Whitelock, centre — sign autographs at the new AMI Stadium just minutes after beating Perth's Western Force 38–24 in the last Super Rugby round robin game of the season on July 14, 2012.

**STACY SQUIRES**

Confidence, however, was not in short supply. Sport New Zealand's Richard Lindsay raised some wry grins with his revelations at an October 2012 forum at Lincoln University on the future provision of sport and recreation in greater Christchurch. Lindsay, a key player in the Sport and Recreation Leadership Group, said all sports in Canterbury were surveyed about the impact of the earthquakes.

'Without a word of a lie, they all said they were going to grow and they all pretty much said they were the fastest growing sport in Canterbury, as well,' Lindsay said. 'And none of them had the evidence to back that up.'

Patience and prudence were the watchwords at the Lincoln forum. Lindsay noted all sports also said they were capable of hosting world championships, but he said they had to be realistic in the rebuild phase. He cited, as an example, the need for new track-cycling facilities in Christchurch with Denton Park now tired and dated. But Lindsay said sports and planners also had to weigh up whether a small country like New Zealand should or could support another international-standard velodrome when two already existed, in Invercargill and Waikato.

As 2013 dawned, the Canterbury sporting sector — the possessor of such a storied past — was again aiming high. ∎

# ARTS
## FINDING SOLACE IN CREATIVITY

*Christopher Moore*

By early 2010, it had become apparent that Christchurch was emerging as New Zealand's cultural hub … and no one was laughing at the suggestion. The city that had once been home to a number of pioneering modernist artists including Rita Angus, Bill Sutton and Colin McCahon was now rediscovering its voice and a new vitality.

**THEATRE, THE VISUAL** arts and music were flowering in the hands of a new generation of innovative and imaginative artists. From Christchurch Art Gallery's gleaming glass facade and sophisticated interiors to the web of small studio spaces in the city's old commercial buildings, Christchurch's burgeoning reputation as an artistic leader was being fuelled. Its reputation as a fustian, conservative and unadventurous place was contradicted by the current of quirky, challenging and innovative creativity that flowed beneath the staid facade.

The Court Theatre, and its newly formed wing at The Forge, had emerged as major forces in New Zealand theatre. Southern Opera was returning live performances to the city. The former Canterbury Society of Arts had evolved into the Centre of Contemporary Art, with its exciting exhibition spaces. A catalogue of artists featured names like Bill Hammond, Julia Morison, Philip Trusttum, Phil Price, Darryn George and Tony de Lautour. Students at the University of Canterbury's School of Fine Arts and the Christchurch Polytechnic Institute of Technology (CPIT) were adding their energy and creativity to the city's cultural engine.

Everything shifted irrevocably in the cold pre-dawn hours of September 4, 2010. Many artists lost their studio spaces as a large number of the city's older buildings disintegrated in the earthquake. Christchurch Art Gallery was drafted into active service as the Civil Defence headquarters. Other

**LEFT** Repiling of the Christchurch Art Gallery under way. The gallery acted as civil defence headquarters after the September 2010 and February 2011 quakes but was then closed after engineers found its floor was no longer level.
**DON SCOTT**

**MIDDLE** Officials from civil defence, government agencies, emergency services and the Christchurch City Council took up residence in the Art Gallery after the quakes.
**CARYS MONTEATH**

galleries and performance spaces closed temporarily as the arts community, like other Cantabrians, picked itself up and carried on, defying the damage and rejoicing that no lives had been lost.

As the psychological and physical scars were repaired during the weeks that followed, the galleries reopened. A group of artists, including Tony de Lautour and Mike Hewson, returned to studio spaces in the former Government Life Building overlooking Cathedral Square. The Court opened a new season, while audiences packed the Isaac Theatre Royal to see Sir Ian McKellen appearing in *Waiting for Godot*. But nature had a continuing role to play in this unfolding drama.

At 12.51pm on Tuesday, February 22, 2011, any sense of returning normalcy descended into the rubble and dust. While de Lautour and his fellow artists fled from their studios, the Court Theatre's staff and actors huddled outside their badly damaged theatre in the Arts Centre. The Christchurch Art Gallery seemed to lurch sideways as a succession of seismic waves struck. At the intersection of High St and Manchester St, Phil Price's kinetic sculpture *Nucleus* still stood amid the devastation, its red petals continuing to turn, transforming the sculpture into a symbol of resilience.

As she joined the evacuation from the central city, artist Jane Zusters began to take a series of photographs of shattered buildings which eventually became the focus of a new exhibition. In Sydenham, photographer Doc Ross

*In terms of performance and exhibition spaces, the quake and its aftershocks exacted a terrible price from the city's arts community. Not one of its theatres was unscathed.*

**LEFT** The sculpture on the corner of High St and Manchester St stands tall while buildings around lay in ruins. The Westpac tower has since been demolished.
**JOHN KIRK-ANDERSON**

**TOP** Repair work gets under way on the badly damaged Isaac Theatre Royal in Gloucester St.
**DAVID HALLETT**

**BOTTOM** Parts of Christchurch's much-loved Town Hall have moved and its basement is filled with silt and sand from liquefaction, but the city council still hopes to repair and renovate part of the complex.
**DEAN KOZANIC**

refused to leave his home and studio. For several months, Ross and his wife would be among the suburb's few permanent residents.

In terms of performance and exhibition spaces, the quake and its aftershocks exacted a terrible price from the city's arts community. Not one of its theatres was unscathed. The 88-year-old landmark Repertory Theatre in Kilmore St lay in ruins. The Isaac Theatre Royal suffered major damage, but strengthening completed a decade before saved the historic theatre from total collapse.

Christchurch Town Hall was mauled and unusable. The Court lost its theatre, with the bulk of its wardrobe, props and technical equipment. Most of the city's dealer galleries were left abandoned inside the red zone. There were also the many individual losses to artists' work and performing spaces, homes and materials. The earthquake's scars were etched permanently into the city's collective psyche.

As increasing numbers of artists left the city, Christchurch faced a looming cultural crisis at a time when the arts had the potential to play a major role in the mental and physical recovery from New Zealand's largest and most destructive natural disaster.

In the following weeks, small miracles inched up through the dust and rubble. Coralie Winn and her unsinkable Gap Filler (GF) team began to inhabit abandoned spaces with quirky, eye-catching installations and temporary creative projects. If nature abhors a vacuum, Winn loathes them, especially those that appeared in this city that had been profoundly reshaped by a major natural disaster.

'Empty or vacant spaces, whether land or in buildings, are a killer for any city,' Winn has said. 'What we are offering is activation of these spaces, to revitalise and regenerate these spaces for the community with all manner of creative projects.

'People from the community seem to want to get involved with GF and support it because it is a grass-roots initiative. This is our strength. We are not a top-down initiative.'

On February 22, Winn was in her home when the walls suddenly collapsed around her. 'I remained in a fog for several days afterwards. All I could think about was where was I going to get water and whether I could go back into the house to retrieve things. Then I wanted to get Gap Filler going again. It was the only way ahead.'

One of the city's oldest and most highly respected dealer galleries came to life in a small suburban street after owner Jonathan Smart and sculptor Neil Dawson joined forces in Dawson's England St studio. It was more than a gesture of defiance — it was a rallying call for others to follow.

One of the earliest responses to the cultural disaster came from an unexpected quarter. Creative New Zealand, often dismissed as a remote, slow-moving bureaucracy, moved quickly to recognise the potential damage caused by a continued exodus of artists from the city. Led by chief executive Stephen Wainwright and New Zealand Arts Council chair Alistair Carruthers, Creative New Zealand staff arrived in Christchurch for the first of many visits to provide logistical, financial and, most importantly, moral support to the stressed arts community. The agency quickly formed an earthquake emergency response fund to help creative ventures get back on their feet. The financial support enabled subsidised ticket prices to be offered for events, including the Christchurch Arts Festival, while also providing some economic security to artists and organisations.

But Wainwright saw the rebuilding of an art infrastructure as a priority: 'We already know that the arts have the power to entertain and enhance a sense of well-being. It has been essential for the people of Christchurch in these incredibly difficult times to find solace in creative activity.'

Grants have included $40,000 to help the World Buskers Festival Trust relocate to Hagley Park and $12,957 to support a fundraiser for mobile galleries. By late 2011, 12 grants totalling $660,000 had been approved to

> *'We already know that the arts have the power to entertain and enhance a sense of well-being. It has been essential for the people of Christchurch in these incredibly difficult times to find solace in creative activity.'*

**TOP** The founder of the Gap Filler scheme, Coralie Winn, looks over another site.
**DAVID HALLETT**

**MIDDLE TOP** Impromptu piano concerts started attracting audiences at Gap Filler sites around the city, like this one in which Tim Driver played for Woolston residents.
**DEAN KOZANIC**

**MIDDLE BOTTOM** Gap Filler director Coralie Winn takes control of the Dance-o-Mat on the corner of St Asaph and Manchester streets.
**DON SCOTT**

**BOTTOM** Another Gap Filler project offering ten-pin bowling with a difference on the site of a demolished old pub on the corner of Madras and St Asaph streets.
**DAVID HALLETT**

help re-establish an active arts scene in the city.

But the arts now faced some hard decisions to ensure their survival. As Alistair Carruthers observed at the launch of the 2011 SCAPE Biennial, the arts were not a peripheral sideshow to this complex process. They were an integral partner and the authorities involved in the process, notably the Christchurch Earthquake Recovery Authority (CERA), ignored this fact at their peril.

From Auckland, writer, art critic and former Cantabrian Hamish Keith quickly launched an initiative to establish a website to catalogue artworks lost or mislaid since the September quake.

By April 2011, homeless arts organisations were already sharing free office space at CPIT while decisions on future venues were made. The Christchurch Arts Festival Trust, the Christchurch Symphony Orchestra, the Body Festival, the SCAPE Physics Room, the World Buskers Festival, the Christchurch Writers Festival, Arts on Tour New Zealand, the Christchurch Music Industry Trust, the Christchurch City Choir and Creative New Zealand all found themselves sharing office space. A joint dialogue had begun on the city's cultural recovery.

The most pressing need for the city's arts was emergency studio and performance spaces. Warren Feeney, the former director of the Centre of Contemporary Art, and his colleague Ron Mottram decided to construct much-needed artists' studios at their new 241 Chambers Gallery in Moorhouse Ave. They were approached by Grant Close, owner-operator of Riccarton PlaceMakers, with the offer of help, labour and materials to create five studios in the former furniture shop. Close, a self-confessed country boy with little previous involvement with art and artists, had become fascinated by this new world when introduced to it by his wife.

A skein of dealer galleries also continued to provide much-needed exhibition spaces — often in totally unexpected places, defying unpredictable lease arrangements and continuing large aftershocks. Four friends not long out of Canterbury's School of Fine Arts — Matt Akehurst, Zhonghao Chen, Oscar Enberg and Sebastian Warne — opened a two-room exhibition space in Addington. They named it ABC — a title that was straightforward and to the point — and designer Matt Galloway created a typographical font for it.

'It was an idea that germinated while at art school,' Akehurst explained. 'The four of us used to hang out together and discuss the possibility of starting a gallery after our studies.'

At the time, the diaspora from the central city to the western suburbs saw many creative spirits migrating to the industrial area. ABC was intended as a place to show a select number of exhibitions and projects each year — from emerging and established artists locally, nationally and internationally — to promote and provoke. The rest of Christchurch's art scene was hunkered down in damage control, or simply catatonic.

As *Press* arts critic Andrew Paul Wood reported, the new gallery was a much-needed tonic. The opening night was packed with people desperate for a point of contact and sense of community. 'A lot of people equated us to starting the gallery as a response to the earthquake; this is not the case,' Akehurst said. 'However, we found ourselves in the situation of providing Christchurch with an artist-run space in a time of need and counted ourselves fortunate to be in this situation and tried to provide hope for artists that not all was lost in the city.

'The first show was postponed due to the February earthquake but we worked through aftershocks and our own personal earthquake-related difficulties to get it out as soon as we could.'

By September 2011, ABC had opened a reading room to allow the region's arts community to access those hard-to-find publications through which the international avant-garde talks about itself. All of this has done much to keep the avant-garde spirit alive in the Christchurch art scene. Later the Lincoln Rd building was sold pending demolition. But the project by these four young Cantabrians left an enduring memory.

Theatre also came onstage to boost battered spirits. The Free Theatre of Christchurch presented a critically acclaimed production of *The Earthquake in Chile* in St Mary's Anglican Church in Addington, while Repertory Theatre presented *Julius Caesar* at Burnside High School's Aurora Centre. Despite losing its performing space in the Isaac Theatre Royal, the show went on for Showbiz Christchurch.

Meanwhile an ambitious project to restore the grande dame of city

**(FOLLOWING PAGE, CLOCKWISE)**
**TOP LEFT** Rockfalls have narrowed the road into and out of Sumner but container art brightens the rough journey past Peacocks Gallop.
**DAVID HALLETT**

**TOP MIDDLE ABOVE** Petunias brighten a demolition site in a Gap Filler project on Selwyn St just off Brougham St.
**STACY SQUIRES**

**TOP MIDDLE BELOW** Flowers sprout from road cones on the first anniversary of the February 22, 2011 quake in New Brighton where Bower Ave, Travis Rd and Rockwood Ave meet.
**JOSEPH JOHNSON**

**TOP RIGHT** A telling comment on what many feel lies beneath Christchurch — an art work by Jason Kelly in Sumner.
**KIRK HARGREAVES**

**BOTTOM RIGHT** Container Love coordinator Christine Reitze of Sumner stands on top of the giant knitted quilt covering a shipping container at Peacocks Gallop.
**DAVID HALLETT**

theatres was underway by the middle of 2012. The Isaac Theatre Royal suffered extensive damage during the February and June 2011 quakes, some of which was worsened by the December 23 aftershocks. Emergency repairs have been carried out to stabilise the theatre and enable permanent repairs to be made.

'The heritage aspect of the Isaac Theatre Royal is vitally important in light of the ever-growing loss of so many heritage buildings in the city,' the theatre's general manager, Neil Cox, has said. 'Where possible, the team is working to either preserve or faithfully reconstruct the auditorium and foyer spaces so that when complete they will look substantially the same as they did prior to the earthquake, with some very noticeable new improvements.'

*'The heritage aspect of the Isaac Theatre Royal is vitally important in light of the ever-growing loss of so many heritage buildings in the city,' the theatre's general manager, Neil Cox, has said.*

The repairs will provide quake resistance 'significantly in excess' of building code requirements. 'This will be unique for a heritage building, making it one of the safest and strongest theatres in 21st-century New Zealand,' Cox promised.

While the theatre was insured for the reinstatement of the quake damage, the Theatre Royal Charitable Foundation and the Isaac Theatre Royal launched a fundraising campaign to cover the policy excess, thought to be about $500,000, and improvement costs of about $5.5 million. Even the news that the theatre would not open until at least 2014 did not dent Cox's boundless optimism. The theatre had hoped to open a transitional 'bare-box structure', with seating for about 800 people, between July and September 2013, providing a venue for the Christchurch Arts Festival, the Royal New Zealand Ballet anniversary and the NBR New Zealand Opera's return to Christchurch. The plan was then to close for about eight months to allow complete restoration before the theatre reopened in the second quarter of 2014. However, these plans were abandoned as the rebuild budget increased from $28.6 million to nearly $30 million.

Meanwhile a Creative New Zealand survey in May 2012 reported a significant decline in the number of Christchurch residents attending arts and cultural events since the February 2011 earthquake. However, 90 per cent saw arts and culture as vital to the city's recovery, and 94 per cent agreed it was important for Christchurch to be recognised for excellence in the arts.

A fledgling lobby group, Arts Voice Christchurch, wasted no time in making its presence felt. After initial hesitancy, it emerged as a robust and energetic leader, launching a 2012/13 summer season of music, entertainment and art in the Re:Start Mall, fostering debates and

**BOTTOM MIDDLE** Pete Majendie installed 185 white chairs on the site of the demolished Oxford Tce Baptist Church to poignantly reflect each life lost in the February quake.
**CARYS MONTEATH**

**MIDDLE LEFT** Cathedral Square's famous chessboard was relaunched by Gap Filler and Canterbury University students in Sydenham in November 2011. Volunteers Lewis Carswell, 5, right, brother Heath, 8, and Richard Moreham place the pieces.
**DEAN KOZANIC**

**BOTTOM LEFT** Green Zone art piece by Jason Kelly on Hackthorne Rd in Cashmere.
**KIRK HARGREAVES**

BUILD IT ON

JELLY

JELLY CORPORATION

community forums and keeping art and artists in the public eye.

In a post-earthquake submission on the future of the arts in Christchurch, the group said Christchurch's arts were no longer tagged 'nice to have' but unequivocally labelled 'essential — wanted on journey to re-make Christchurch as the country's cultural capital'.

'Historically the city has produced innovative and influential arts practice. However, these grass-roots appearances are all too often stifled and unsustained. This is the fault of an underdeveloped and poorly implemented council arts policy,' the submission continued.

'While larger organisations receive considerable support, medium and smaller organisations and emerging artists — the wellspring of a diverse and innovative arts culture — find it difficult to operate in Christchurch. This leads to a movement away from the city, not just of artists but the young in general. It is essential that the council invest greater time and attention to developing an arts vision, policy and strategy. The policy must be sustainable, innovative and begin with an insistence that the arts are central to the rebuilding effort.'

What Christchurch needs, according to Arts Voice, is investment in 'a coherent, long ranging and ongoing arts policy with regularly assessed and critiqued milestones . . . achieved with a conversation in the form of a working group'.

'We desperately need to entice innovative, diverse national and international artists and practitioners to Christchurch to enliven both arts

**LEFT** International tenor Placido Domingo sang and charmed more than 8000 people at the CBS Arena in July 2011.
**DON SCOTT**

**MIDDLE LEFT** Welsh mezzo-soprano Katherine Jenkins also sang at the concert.
**DON SCOTT**

practice and broader social life. We need to work immediately on inviting innovative international artists to take part in the re-build, leading to a sustained residency programme. This will completely overturn the city's previous reputation and attract the young and the bold.'

Inspired by the mesh of waterways flowing through Christchurch, the arts lobby group also offered a new vision for the city's post-earthquake arts and cultural life. Its 'River of Arts' concept was based around a series of interconnected arts-based initiatives as well as established and new spaces that integrate the arts into the city's fabric. In a discussion paper, Arts Voice described the proposal as 'an overarching vision to inspire hope and excitement about the city, one that relies on a co-ordinated and collaborative approach by the arts community and related industry and business'.

In its proposal, the 'river' would run from a performance space in the Botanical Gardens, through the Cultural Precinct (Canterbury Museum, the Arts Centre, Christchurch Art Gallery, Centre of Contemporary Art), through Ngai Tahu's proposed cultural centre on the old King Edward's Barracks site, intersecting with the Avon via the Cambridge Terrace cycle-walkway beside the Bridge of Remembrance, and meander toward and perhaps beyond the CPIT. This was brave stuff.

**IF EVIDENCE WAS** needed that the arts were on the road back to recovery, it was provided by one of the world's great operatic tenors and a theatre company's

determination that the show must go on. In July 2011, Placido Domingo charmed and dazzled an audience of more than 8000 in the CBS Canterbury Arena. The concert, which also featured the National Youth Orchestra and Welsh mezzo-soprano Katherine Jenkins, held special significance for Domingo, who lost four relatives in the 1985 Mexico City earthquake. Domingo had been invited to perform by Southern Opera Trust chairman and acclaimed New Zealand singer Christopher Doig, who refused to let advanced bowel cancer prevent him from attending the concert.

'I wish I was simply here for a concert, a normal concert, which I do around the world, but unfortunately I am here because of circumstance in February,' Domingo said. 'I'm very happy I can help to ease the pain and to get together to make beautiful music and to try for a little while to forget about, and see what we can do with the results of the concert.'

The CBS Arena continued to play a significant part in Christchurch's cultural recovery, proving that, with a small amount of tweaking, even a sports stadium could host a concert version of Wagner's *Die Walküre*, the Royal New Zealand Ballet, and a powerful performance of Shostakovich's *Leningrad Symphony* by the New Zealand Symphony Orchestra.

A short distance away, an empty, dusty former Addington grain store was about to undergo one of the most ambitious transformation scenes in the city's theatrical history. The Court Theatre didn't put a foot wrong — or seemingly draw breath — in a smooth scenery change that saw it viewing, arranging, converting and opening a new theatre in Addington within months. Led by its chief executive, Philip Aldridge, The Court had taken a 15-year lease, with three-year renewable terms, on the building. The Shed was built in 16 weeks at a cost of about $4.62 million.

What was once an echoing 2800-square-metre, 10-metre-high space now accommodated a 300-seat auditorium and performance spaces. The Court's auditorium, constructed in a self-contained 'cube' in the centre of the building, provided greater height and depth with an understage. The refit also used Portacoms and containers to provide office space, a box office and a bar in an expansive front of house. The foyer could accommodate an extra stage and provide gallery spaces for other arts organisations. But all this was simply a beginning. The Court, Aldridge promised, would one day return to the central city. Meanwhile it could continue to conjure up that old theatrical magic.

Elsewhere the effects of the disaster continued to be felt. The indefinite closure of Christchurch Art Gallery caused a major fissure in the city's cultural landscape. As director Jenny Harper and her staff kept the gallery in the public eye through a series of website blogs and al fresco exhibitions directed from temporary offices, the city council announced a $36.7 million

project to earthquake-proof the gallery. The building had served as Civil Defence headquarters in the weeks after the September 2010 and February 2011 quakes, and initially it was thought to have escaped unscathed. Engineers later found, however, that while it had suffered no major structural damage, the building was no longer level.

The building would have to be jacked up so that it could be levelled, and base-isolation technology would be installed to lessen its exposure to ground motion in another major quake. The glass facade, wall cladding, parapets above the Worcester Boulevard side, and ceilings and fittings in the foyer and in some galleries had also sustained damage during the December 23 quakes. In May 2012, Christchurch City Council community services general manager Michael Aitken said the time frame for doing the repairs and other necessary work was not yet clear.

Harper described working in a public art gallery without the public as the hardest thing she had ever done. 'When the staff meeting was told that there would be further delays, there was an initial silence. Hopes had been dashed again. But before the meeting finished, there was a determination to push ahead with alternative plans.

'It's really hard to work in an art gallery which is closed to the public. It's tough for the CAG team . . . At our core, we are exhibitionists. We enjoy putting on good shows . . . We enjoy working with artists and making a major contribution to the city's cultural and economic health.'

Defiance also became the unofficial motto for the 2011 Christchurch Arts Festival, held in July that year. Based in Hagley Park, the programme was extended over several weekends rather than being compressed into two weeks. The festival's director, Philip Tremewan, and his team offered an innovative programme of events aimed at a diverse audience. The community needed events that, for a few brief hours, would remind it of the inventive human spirit that even earthquakes and snowstorms could not destroy.

But good fortune was not on the side of the 2011 SCAPE Biennale of Art in Public Space. Postponed after the September 4 quake, battered by the events of February 22, it finally went ahead in a somewhat depleted form later in the year. While some works were transferred to Auckland, Christchurch's artistic landscape became even leaner after the focal point — a magisterial wall hanging by Darryn George on the side of the city council building in Hereford St — was badly damaged by high winds and heavy snow. It was repaired and rehung but eventually succumbed to the elements.

The organisers of the Body Festival of Dance and Physical Theatre refused to let the conditions defeat them, displaying considerable sangfroid to stage programmes in 2011 and 2012 that fused artistic excellence with energy and more than a dash of the old razzle-dazzle. There can't have been many arts festivals with performances of contemporary dance inspired by seismic upheavals, or a rollerskating extravaganza like the one staged at New Brighton Pier.

In August 2012 — a year after the city council issued its Central City Plan following the Share an Idea project — the long-awaited Christchurch Central Development Unit's recovery plan proposed a performing arts precinct to 'accommodate a range of facilities in the event the Christchurch Town Hall cannot be repaired'. An integrated performing arts precinct would run north from Cathedral Square up to the Avon River. The proposal includes a replacement town hall with two auditoriums, the larger shrunk from 2500 seats to a more manageable 1500, the smaller seating 500. The complex could provide a permanent home for the Court Theatre, the Christchurch Symphony Orchestra and the Music Centre of Christchurch.

The proposal fuelled the debate over the future of the existing Christchurch Town Hall, and in November 2012 the city council voted to press ahead with plans to restore and renovate the building — despite suggestions that the government and CERA might block the idea. The land in Victoria Square was badly damaged — liquefaction fills the Town Hall's basement. Ngai Tahu also wants the area for its planned Te Puna Ahurea cultural centre.

Among the victims of the closure of the Town Hall was the southern hemisphere's largest international cello competition, the Christchurch-based New Zealand International Cello Festival and Competition. The events had been held in the Great Hall at the Christchurch Arts Centre and in the Christchurch Town Hall. The organisers considered alternative venues but felt that much of the heart of the festival and competition lay in these particular places. The risk of future aftershocks added to the layer of uncertainty, especially for judges and competitors travelling from overseas.

The Town Hall had also been a performing base for the Christchurch Symphony Orchestra. When the earthquakes occurred the CSO had seemed poised to finally get a home of its own after years using a succession of offices and practice rooms. Most recently, the CSO's management team and music library had been lodged in the Arts Centre complex while its musicians rehearsed at Canterbury University's College of Education.

However, two years earlier the orchestra had been negotiating a deal to take over the Salvation Army Citadel building on the edge of Victoria Square. The city council had agreed to provide $2 million of the $5.25 million needed for a long-term lease in partnership with Southern Opera and Christchurch City Choir. Under the proposal, the CSO's offices and rehearsal rooms would finally come together beneath one roof — in a building that also included a 350-seat auditorium, to be used for smaller recitals and educational visits.

Despite the human and physical dislocation caused by the earthquakes, the CSO did not lose any of its 60 or so players during the following tumultuous two and a half years. It stayed together to stage an emotional 2011 trip to Japan as an international guest of Asia Orchestra Week. The highlight came when the tour was extended to include a concert in Sendai, one of the cities most affected by the March 2011 earthquake and tsunami. The concert, in which the CSO performed alongside the Sendai Philharmonic Orchestra, came after performances by the CSO Brass Quintet — Bruce Roberts (trumpet), Daniel Maxwell (trumpet), Bernie Shapiro (French horn), Karl Margevka (trombone) and Nigel Seaton (tuba) — in various locations, including an impromptu concert for the Sendai Defence Force. The Japanese search and rescue teams were among the first to assist Christchurch after the February 22 quake but had to return to Japan after the March disaster there. The New Zealand musicians were welcomed by a brass quintet from an army band who burst into a welcoming fanfare. Both ensembles then played unrehearsed and without a common language, linked by the shared experience of a devastating natural disaster.

In another footnote, Mike Hewson, one of the artists who evacuated their studios in the Government Life Building on February 22, returned to Christchurch to install his own tribute to the city's cultural and artistic life. Hewson was sharing a studio with his brother Andrew when the magnitude 6.3 earthquake demolished the tower of the neighbouring ChristChurch Cathedral and forced them to flee.

Using the photos of the friends and artists who were working around

**ABOVE** The now demolished Cranmer Courts were the site of an installation by artist Mike Hewson.
**DAVID HALLETT**

**MIDDLE** Artist and engineer Mike Hewson brought life back into the doomed Cranmer Courts for a while.
**DAVID HALLETT**

**RIGHT** Two huge bulls on grand pianos along Madras St, part of a Christchurch Art Gallery exhibition at the nearby Ng Gallery, stopped motorists in their tracks.
**JOHN KIRK-ANDERSON**

him, Hewson turned Cranmer Courts, the former Christchurch Normal School, into a huge canvas showing one man's lament for a city's lost heart and his celebration of the resilience of the creative spirit. Covering a total area of between 120 and 130 square metres, the mixed media images on plywood transformed the abandoned building into something full of life and vibrancy. During their installation Hewson, an engineer as well as an artist, became a familiar figure as, hard hat securely in place, he carefully negotiated the walls of the damaged building on a large mechanical hoist.

A few weeks later, Hewson's images disappeared as Cranmer Courts was demolished. But once again, the memory of what a young Cantabrian had created has endured.

By the end of 2012, the arts had definitely returned to the city's life. NBR New Zealand Opera opened a Christchurch office, Christchurch Art Gallery was planning a continuing series of outreach exhibitions, and the Court was experiencing a sell-out season of the musical *Grease*. A vibrant wall mural by Australian artist Ash Keating added an explosion of colour to what had been

---

*Using the photos of the friends and artists who were working around him, Hewson turned Cranmer Courts, the former Christchurch Normal School, into a huge canvas showing one man's lament for a city's lost heart and his celebration of the resilience of the creative spirit.*

---

New South Wales visitors John and Lorraine admire the work by Melbourne artist Ash Keating on a concrete wall made visible by demolition. The abstract painting was created by throwing, spraying and firing paint from buckets, weed sprayers and fire extinguishers.

**STACY SQUIRES**

―――――

*A city is not simply composed of buildings. It's a composite landscape of history, human experience and aspirations that even natural or man-made disasters cannot eradicate. What we make of it is up to us.*

―――――

a drab inner-city site.

In an interview in 2011, architect and urban planner David Sim was asked whether Christchurch could be reborn and rebuilt from a blank canvas. No such thing existed, the plain-speaking Scot replied. A city is not simply composed of buildings. It's a composite landscape of history, human experience and aspirations that even natural or man-made disasters cannot eradicate. What we make of it is up to us.

Nowhere is this more true than in the arts, where human emotions, beliefs and imagination are made tangible. In small and large ways, individually and collectively, Christchurch's arts community reacted to an unfolding human disaster with innovation and resilience, proving beyond any doubt that the arts have played — and will continue to play — a pivotal role in the city's recovery. ■